MEDLINE:
A Basic Guide to Searching

MEDLINE:
A Basic Guide to Searching

by Susan J. Feinglos

Medical Library Association, Inc.
Chicago, Illinois

MLA Information Series

National Library of Medicine Cataloging in Publication

Z
699.5.M39
F299m

Feinglos, Susan J.
    MEDLINE, a basic guide to searching / by Susan
J. Feinglos. — Chicago, Ill.: Medical Library
Association, c1985.

    Bibliography: p.
    Includes index.
    ISBN 0-912176-19-9.
    1. MEDLARS-MEDLINE Information System   I. Title.

ISBN 0-912176-19-9

FOR MY SISTER, PAM

CONTENTS

FIGURES

Preface

The purpose of *MEDLINE: A Basic Guide to Searching* is to introduce new MEDLINE searchers to the biomedical database MEDLINE. Experienced MEDLINE searchers may find it valuable as a review.

This book is divided into six sections: 1) a brief overview of online searching; 2) an introduction to MEDLINE, which describes its history, providers, comparison with *Index Medicus,* and contents; 3) *MeSH: Medical Subject Headings;* 4) software features; 5) search strategy formulation; and 6) sample search strategies.

To use MEDLINE, searchers must know how the thesaurus terms are chosen, and then use the appropriate terms, software commands, and strategies. A new MEDLINE searcher recently told me that he was doing "great" searches for topics such as "treatment of kidney stones in children" by searching for the words "treatment," "children," "kidney," and "stones." He was unaware of MeSH indexing principles: the subheadings for treatment such as THERAPY, DRUG THERAPY, SURGERY, RADIO-THERAPY, etc.; the age-specific tags (known as "check tags") such as CHILD; CHILD, PRESCHOOL; INFANT; and of the most important term of all—KIDNEY CALCULI. This new searcher did not use the full capabilities of MEDLINE and never uncovered the universe of information on the topics for which he searched. (This search is described in Chapter Six, Sample Search Strategies 2 and 3.)

It is hoped that this short, practical book will provide the basics of MEDLINE in one source. The National Library of Medicine and the commercial database vendors Bibliographic Retrieval Services and DIA-LOG offer more detailed information through MEDLINE training sessions, training workbooks, manuals, newsletters, and telephone user desk service.

MEDLINE, like any other database, can be expensive to search. Cost-effective techniques for all aspects of the search process are described throughout this book. For certain search topics, other databases may be more appropriate or should be used in addition to MEDLINE. Unfortunately, these additional databases are beyond the scope of this book.

Glossary terms are italicized at their first occurrence throughout this book. Input examples are numbered when necessary to show a sequence of steps. These examples will often vary from system to system, though they provide the same information. A searcher's input is shown in upper case characters to distinguish it from the text. In actuality, either upper or lower case characters can be used in online searching as long as the correct characters are used. Representations of the entire MEDLINE search process, including searcher prompts and search results, are shown in the sample search strategies presented in Chapter Six.

The largest problem involved in writing an online reference work is currency—this book will be no exception. Please check with the vendors for the most up-to-the-minute information.

I would like to thank all my fellow staff members at Duke University Medical Center Library—past and present—for their many contributions to this book.

I would also like to acknowledge the expertise and assistance of the staff at the following organizations: Bibliographic Retrieval Services, DIALOG, the Medical Library Association, and the National Library of Medicine.

Parts of this book were initially developed for the MEDLINE section of Literature of the Health Sciences taught at the University of North Carolina at Chapel Hill School of Library Science. I would like to thank Fred Roper and Mary Ann Brown for affording me this opportunity.

Very special thanks go to Joan Grygel, Project Manager, and to everyone who has been part of this project at some point in its progress.

Finally, I would like to thank my husband, Mark, for his patience and understanding.

December 1984
Durham, North Carolina

Chapter One

What Is Online Searching?

Online searching involves the use of computers to retrieve information from machine-readable files, or *databases*. This is an interactive process. That is, a searcher can view results and modify his or her strategy as the search progresses.

BACKGROUND INFORMATION

Databases can be online versions of printed sources of information. For example, MEDLINE is the online version of *Index Medicus* published by the National Library of Medicine (NLM). MEDLINE is a *bibliographic database*. It contains information about the documents (*records*) in it, rather than the documents themselves. Other databases may contain numeric data or even the complete text of documents. Bibliographic Retrieval Services (BRS) in Latham, N.Y., produces a database called COMPREHENSIVE CORE MEDICAL LIBRARY. It contains the complete text of selected textbooks and journals and is an example of a *full-text database.*

Online searching has many advantages: speed; multiple access points; flexibility, or the capability to tailor results to needs; currency; and probably most important of all, convenience. Instead of trying to find information under different subjects in *Index Medicus* volume by volume, and unbound issue by unbound issue, a MEDLINE searcher can simply enter a *search strategy*, modify the strategy if necessary, and print or store the results for later use.

Online searching also has disadvantages: dates of coverage (many bibliographic databases began in the late 1960s or earlier 1970s); currency (many databases, MEDLINE included, can be from six weeks to six months or more behind the published literature); retrieval problems due to database contents, indexing weaknesses, a searcher's lack of skill, or a search topic inappropriate for an online search; and costs.

Companies or organizations marketing online databases are known as *vendors.* NLM both markets and produces databases. BRS and the DIALOG System* are the two other major vendors of biomedically-related databases. BRS also produces a few of its databases.

Today, these three vendors offer more than 300 databases in all major subject areas. Some of their relevant databases in the health sciences include: BIOSIS PREVIEWS (BRS, DIALOG), CANCERLIT (NLM),

*Service Mark Reg. U.S. Patent and Trademark Office.

EXCERPTA MEDICA (BRS, DIALOG), HEALTH PLANNING AND ADMINISTRATION (BRS, DIALOG, NLM), MEDICAL AND PSYCHO-LOGICAL PREVIEWS (BRS), PSYCINFO (BRS, DIALOG), SCISEARCH (DIALOG), and TOXLINE (NLM).

In the past, online searches were usually run by trained information specialists. However, with the advent of the microcomputer (personal computer) and easier to use, or *"user-friendly"* systems, a growing number of *end-users* (the ultimate recipients of the online information) have begun searching for themselves.

To access online databases, you need certain equipment and a password issued by a vendor. The equipment usually includes a computer terminal or a microcomputer, a telephone outlet, a *modem* which connects the computer to the telephone line and converts machine-readable data to a form compatible with telecommunications equipment or vice versa, and—to make microcomputers communicate with other computers—*communications software programs. Software* is a string of instructions that commands a computer to perform certain functions.

Telephone lines are used to transmit data from a computer terminal to a database vendor's host computer and back again. Telecommunication networks like TELENET, TYMNET, and UNINET are used to save the costs of long-distance calls. A printer and/or a *cathode ray tube (CRT)* screen make the results of the online search process visible. These results can be printed on paper or *downloaded*—stored in a user's own computer—depending on copyright restrictions. Detailed information about the type of equipment needed for online searching can be found in vendor manuals.

BOOLEAN LOGIC

Online searching employs *Boolean logic,* a method of logic developed by the English mathematician and logician George Boole (1815–1864). Bool-ean operators combine *sets* or terms in various relationships. The major *logical operators* are: "AND," "OR," and "NOT," ("AND NOT" is used at NLM).

"AND" is used to combine concepts. It will retrieve records containing both terms or sets in a combination. INFLUENZA "AND" COUGH will retrieve articles discussing both concepts. This relationship can be described by the use of a *Venn diagram.* Venn diagrams are named for the British logician John Venn (1834–1923). These diagrams represent logical relationships with circles. See figure 1.1.

"OR" is used to search on all or any concepts. It will retrieve records containing all or any terms in an "ORed" statement. INFLUENZA "OR" COUGH will retrieve all the records about either term. See figure 1.2.

"NOT" ("AND NOT" at NLM) is used to exclude information. INFLUENZA "NOT" COUGH will retrieve all articles on INFLUENZA not indexed to COUGH. See figure 1.3.

Throughout this book, Boolean logic forms the backbone of the search process. The searcher requests sets or terms in individual *search statements* (user-entered queries) to retrieve matching groups of records.

Figure 1.1 Boolean "AND"

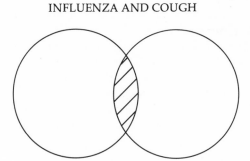

INFLUENZA AND COUGH

Figure 1.2 Boolean "OR"

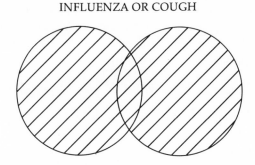

INFLUENZA OR COUGH

Figure 1.3 Boolean "NOT"

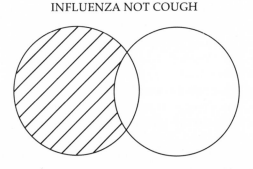

INFLUENZA NOT COUGH

Chapter Two
Introduction to MEDLINE

MEDLINE is the major online database used by health sciences searchers in North America. According to the 1982/83 *Annual Statistics of Medical School Libraries in the United States and Canada,* MEDLINE accounted for 77.95% of all database accesses in these libraries.[1]

A BRIEF HISTORY

In 1964, NLM began using a computerized system for producing its printed publication, *Index Medicus.* Soon after, early searches were run in batches against the computer database. The complete system, producing both NLM's printed and online products, became known as MEDLARS (*MED*ical *L*iterature *A*nalysis and *R*etrieval *S*ystem). NLM began experimenting with direct online searching in 1967. In 1970, an initial online pilot study, *AIM-TWX,* was undertaken using the new publication *Abridged Index Medicus,* a subset of *Index Medicus* containing references to 100 English-language clinical medicine journals. This pilot study was accessed through System Development Corporation (SDC) using the Teletypewriter Exchange Network (TWX). The software used was called ELHILL 1. (*ELHILL* was an acronym for Senator Lister Hill, who, along with then Senator John F. Kennedy, sponsored the legislation creating the National Library of Medicine in 1956.)

MEDLINE (*MED*LARS on*LINE*) (ELHILL 2) superseded AIM-TWX in October 1971. Until 1973, it included only 60% of the material in *Index Medicus.* MEDLARS II, using ELHILL 3 programs, began in January 1975. With each year, improvements and refinements were made to the MEDLARS system. New developments are presently underway for MEDLARS III in 1985.

MEDLINE PROVIDERS

As of December 1984, NLM offered MEDLINE and 21 other online databases. In addition, MEDLINE is offered in the United States by two commercial database vendors: Bibliographic Retrieval Services (BRS) loaded it in January 1977, and DIALOG in May 1981.

MEDLINE is also available in a simplified, user-friendly format, often at reduced rates, through BRS/AFTER DARK, BRS/SAUNDERS COLLEAGUE, DIALOG's KNOWLEDGE INDEX, and Beth Israel Hospital's PAPERCHASE. Information about these user-friendly systems changes frequently. As of this writing, all but DIALOG's KNOWLEDGE INDEX have *menu-driven* software—software aided by a menu of choices for commands and formats. BRS/SAUNDERS COLLEAGUE and PAPER-CHASE are available during daytime hours. (BRS/AFTER DARK will soon be available during the day, rather than only on nights and weekends.)

It is difficult to advise searchers which vendor's MEDLINE—user-friendly or regular—will best serve their needs. The following chapters on the basics of MEDLINE, with search examples taken from the regular, full-featured MEDLINE databases at BRS, DIALOG, and NLM will acquaint you with some of the options available. All MEDLINE searchers, new or experienced, should consider the following when deciding which system(s) to access: costs, hours of operation, search capabilities, years of coverage, other databases also available from the vendor, and ease of learning. A list of MEDLINE vendors and their addresses appears in Appendix A.

Ways to access MEDLINE keep increasing. NLM has begun to offer subsets of the database for storage and re-use; while some institutions offer users their own version of MEDLINE. It is also possible to purchase *database access software*, also referred to as "front end," or "gateway," that makes it easier to use the regular systems by providing an interface between the user and these systems. This software includes: IN-SEARCH (for DIALOG only), SCI-MATE, and ORBIT SEARCHMASTER. See Appendix A for addresses.

MEDLINE instruction is provided by BRS, DIALOG, and NLM. NLM's training is the most comprehensive. Both DIALOG and NLM have specialized online training files for MEDLINE education. DIALOG has a small practice file called ONTAP MEDLINE, while NLM has a computer-assisted instruction database called MEDLEARN, and a small practice file, INTROMED.

COMPARISON BETWEEN INDEX MEDICUS AND MEDLINE

MEDLINE contains the references from *Index Medicus, International Nursing Index, Index to Dental Literature,* and articles from a few journals in the field of communication. Approximately 3300 journal titles are indexed for MEDLINE; 2700 titles are indexed in *Index Medicus.* There are more than 4.2 million records in MEDLINE.

MEDLINE can be searched back to 1966, while *Index Medicus* is available in printed form under various titles back to 1879. Some of the published literature on a topic will not be found online in MEDLINE because of the years it covers. For example, many of the accounts of the use of thalidomide by pregnant women were published before 1966; therefore, searching MEDLINE would not retrieve contemporary articles. (Due to the size of the MEDLINE database, its records are contained in several *backfiles*—older portions of the database—in addition to the current file of references. A list of each vendor's file divisions can be found in Appendix B.)

MEDLINE is one month more up-to-date than *Index Medicus*. Even then, MEDLINE can be from six weeks to six months or more behind the published literature due to the length of the indexing process.

MEDLINE provides more access points to journal articles than *Index Medicus*. While articles can appear in *Index Medicus* under three or four subject headings, the same articles are indexed in greater depth in MEDLINE. Articles have, on the average, 8–10 subject headings in addition to routine concepts or "tags" (*check tags*) such as age, sex, human, animal, etc. MEDLINE articles can also be searched by words from their titles or abstracts, thus making it easier to retrieve concepts that do not have convenient subject headings.

MEDLINE contains online abstracts of approximately 40% of the articles indexed since 1975. These abstracts are the same ones found with the printed articles. *Index Medicus* does not contain abstracts. Neither source contains meeting abstracts.

MEDLINE often makes it possible to search only with the newest version of a subject heading. Using *Index Medicus*, you must look under both the old and new subject heading depending on the year of the volume. For example, MARFAN SYNDROME replaced ARACHNODAC-TYLY in 1985. In MEDLINE, you would be able to use the new subject heading MARFAN SYNDROME to retrieve all the earlier references indexed to ARACHNODACTYLY. Using *Index Medicus*, you would look under both headings depending on the year of the volume.

However, when a new subject heading with no directly-corresponding term is created, such as ELDER ABUSE in 1984, earlier references on this topic are not re-indexed with this heading. More information on searching for new subject headings will be found in Chapter Three, How to Use Medical Subject Headings, and in Chapter Six, Sample Search Strategies.

DESCRIPTION OF CONTENTS

MEDLINE records are composed of numerous *fields*—the categories of information within a single record. Abstracts, authors, and subject headings are examples of fields. This section describes the most important fields for the new searcher. Methods of searching these fields are discussed in detail in Chapter Four, Software Features.

Index Medicus has two points of access: by authors and by subject headings. The following reference to an article appeared in *Index Medicus:*

SAKETKHOO K, JANUSZKIEWICA A, SACKNER MA: Effects of drinking hot water, cold water, and chicken soup on nasal mucus velocity and nasal airflow resistance. Chest 74(4):408–10, Oct 78

In addition to access through authors (SAKETKHOO K, JANUSZKIE-WICA A, SACKNER MA) and subject headings (NASAL MUCOSA; MEDI-CINE, TRADITIONAL; COLD, etc.) MEDLINE users can retrieve this article through title words such as CHICKEN and SOUP. The principles of

MEDLINE indexing—how subject headings are chosen—are discussed in Chapter Three. Following is a brief description of the contents of important fields in MEDLINE. (For the most comprehensive descriptions, review the literature of the MEDLINE system you are using. See Appendix C for a list of online searching aids.)

Abstracts. English-language abstracts of journal articles have been included in MEDLINE since 1975. Approximately 40% of the total database has abstracts. Since 1980, 50% of MEDLINE has abstracts. Abstracts have been included in MEDLINE if the article had an English-language abstract, if abstracts were taken from a particular journal, if permission was granted by the journal publisher,[2] and if the abstract was of the allowed length.

An abstract is included when the journal in which it is published is designated by NLM as *Priority 1* or *Priority 2*, but not *Priority 3*. The *New England Journal of Medicine* is a Priority 1 journal. (Note, however, that NLM does not publish a list of MEDLINE journals by priority ranking.) Priority 1 and 2 journals, constituting 60% of the database, are indexed in depth, and Priority 1 journals are given rush handling due to their importance to the clinician. Priority 3 journals are usually not indexed in as great a depth.

In the past, there were cut-off limits based on the length of an abstract (200, then later 250 words). The abstract was omitted if it exceeded these limits. Now, if an abstract exceeds the limits of 250 words (or 400 words if the article is 10 pages or more, or from a core list of cancer journals), it is merely cut off and no longer totally omitted from MEDLINE as it was in the past.

There are two types of abstract-designators. *ENGLISH ABSTRACT* indicates that an English-language abstract exists for a foreign-language article. This abstract may or may not be online in MEDLINE. The second type of abstract-designator is used to indicate the presence of online abstracts for English and non-English articles; its form varies from vendor to vendor.

Authors. Author names are listed for MEDLINE as they appear on the first page of each article. Last names, as many as two initials, and designations such as JR or 2d can be used. Sometimes it can be difficult to find articles written by a specific author with a common name. For example, Robert, Roberta, and Roy Smith all appear as SMITH R.

There is no standard list of author names in MEDLINE. If an author sometimes uses the designation JR, or sometimes a middle initial, his or her name will appear in MEDLINE in different forms. See Chapter Four, Software Features, for a discussion of comprehensive author search methods.

As of 1984, up to 10 authors of an article are listed in both MEDLINE and *Index Medicus*. Prior to 1977, only the first three authors were listed in *Index Medicus*. Thus MEDLINE is the only source for retrieving any author name beyond the third one listed for those articles.

Authors' Addresses. The address of the first author of an article is available for Priority 1 and 2 journals. The information is taken from the first page of each article. Errors or variations in spellings are not corrected. The author's address is useful for compiling a list of publications of a specific organization or for finding out which author is the correct one due to a common or an unusually spelled last name. BRS contains this information back to 1977, DIALOG back to 1982, and NLM, which gathers these addresses in the indexing process, keeps them only in its *SDILINE* file—a database which contains the latest month's MEDLINE references. The latest month of MEDLINE is also available in NLM's MEDLINE database, but it does not contain authors' addresses.

Journal Subsets. There are two major subsets of MEDLINE: the 117 English-language clinical journals from *Abridged Index Medicus*, and the 1900 Priority 1 and 2 journals. These subsets can be used to limit the results of a MEDLINE search. The latter subset is not available for searching at DIALOG.

Languages. English-language articles presently make up 76% of MED-LINE. Brackets appear around the English translations of foreign-language article titles. Before 1984, translated article titles had the designation (AUTHOR'S TRANSL) after them. At DIALOG, the original foreign-language title will appear as well as the English-language title.

Monographs. Chapters from selected multi-authored monographs were indexed from May 1976 through December 1981; they make up less than 1% of MEDLINE. The call numbers appearing with the monograph reference are those of NLM—not necessarily those of your local medical library.

Registry Numbers and Enzyme Numbers. Chemical Abstract Services (CAS) registry numbers and Enzyme Commission (EC) numbers have been searchable since June 1980 in MEDLINE. Both numbers print out with the *name of substance.* The name of substance is the preferred name of a chemical or drug, usually the generic name. *Registry and enzyme numbers* provide more specific access to many substances indexed to a broader drug or chemical name.

Indexing information about these substances can be found in NLM's online database MeSH VOCABULARY FILE, or in NLM's printed publication, *Medical Subject Headings—Supplementary Chemical Records.*

Source. The abbreviated journal title, the year, month, volume, issue, and pages of a reference make up the source field. Individual components of the source field such as journal title and year can also be searched. Volume, issue, and page numbers can be searched at BRS and NLM. This is useful for verifying a partial reference.

Special List Indicators. Articles indexed from approximately 600 non-*Index Medicus* journals are included in MEDLINE and are given a *special list indicator.* Special list indicators are assigned to the non-*Index Medicus* journals from the following MEDLINE subsets: 1) *Index to Dental Literature,*

2) *International Nursing Index,* 3) communication disorders, and 4) foreign centers. Most MEDLINE searchers will need to use only the dental and nursing special list indicators.

Subject Headings. Indexing is done by subject specialists who assign *subject headings* (MeSH terms) from *Medical Subject Headings (MeSH)* using indexing principles created by the National Library of Medicine. MeSH terms can be made the major point of an article. MeSH terms can also have *subheadings,* subdivisions of MeSH terms that group together important aspects of MeSH terms. Subject headings and subheadings are discussed in greater detail in Chapters Three and Four.

Textwords. The individual words found in the titles and abstracts of MEDLINE references are known as *textwords.* They are computer-generated and "text-edited" depending on the specific rules of each vendor. Basically, all special characters—commas, periods, slashes, etc.—are converted to blanks. For example, "high-risk" is composed of two textwords: "high" and "risk." The number of *stopwords*—common, non-significant words such as "the" that are ignored by the computer in textword searching—varies from system to system. See Appendix D for a list of each vendor's stopwords. See also Chapter Four for a discussion of specific textword generation rules.

Titles. Individual words in article titles are searchable based on textword generation rules. As discussed in the language field above, foreign-language article titles only appear in their original language at DIALOG, where the individual foreign words are also searchable.

Years. The year of publication is searchable in MEDLINE. In addition, the month an article became part of the MEDLINE database is also searchable. There is a time lag between the date an article is published and the actual date that it enters the MEDLINE system. For example, all the articles entered in MEDLINE in 1984 do not have a publication year of 1984. Some will be dated 1983, some 1982, and a few, even earlier.

Notes

[1]Derived from: Lyders R, ed. Statistics of medical school libraries in the United States and Canada, 1982–1983. 6th ed. Houston: Association of Academic Health Sciences Library Directors, 1983:77–8.

[2]Pergamon Press (1982) and Academic Press (1983) were the last two publishers to grant NLM permission to use their abstracts in MEDLINE.

Chapter Three

How to Use Medical Subject Headings

The references in MEDLINE and *Index Medicus* are indexed with Medical Subject Headings (MeSH terms) using the tools and principles discussed in this chapter. Searchers need to know how terms are chosen and then use appropriate search strategies to retrieve specific topics. NLM's annual publication *Medical Subject Headings (MeSH)* provides the foundation of this process. NLM's *MEDLARS Indexing Manual* is the source of all indexing rules for MEDLINE.

The expanded version of *MeSH*, known as the *Annotated MeSH*, is essential to the efficient use of MEDLINE. It contains three parts: a) *Medical Subject Headings, Annotated Alphabetic List*, b) *Tree Structures*, and c) *Permuted Medical Subject Headings*. A smaller, single-volume *MeSH* appears as Part Two of the January issue of *Index Medicus* and is called the "black-and-white" *MeSH* because of the color of its cover.

Ideally, the three volumes of the *Annotated MeSH* should be purchased annually because MeSH terms are routinely added, deleted, and changed each year. Earlier editions should be retained as they contain information about the way new MeSH terms were previously indexed.

In addition to the printed tools, both DIALOG and NLM have online MeSH vocabulary files. Only NLM's—the MeSH VOCABULARY FILE—is a separate database which is automatically interactive with MEDLINE. Through special programming with the MeSH VOCABULARY FILE it is possible to search in NLM's MEDLINE using variations of MeSH terms not found in the MEDLINE database.

A list of useful printed tools for the MEDLINE searcher is found in Appendix E. Annotations are provided for tools not described in this chapter.

THE THREE SECTIONS OF THE ANNOTATED MeSH

The Annotated Alphabetic List

The *Annotated Alphabetic List* currently contains more than 14,600 subject headings and 10,000 cross references. Many of the subject headings are annotated. However, it contains neither full definitions of terms nor sufficient cross references. Scope notes that provide the meaning of many of the terms can be found online in the MeSH VOCABULARY FILE (at NLM only), in some NLM inhouse scope note compilations, and in a compilation of scope notes from 1972–1984.[1]

The following example from the *Annotated Alphabetic List* in figure 3.1 shows part of the page in which the MeSH term SPORTS is found.

Figure 3.1   Excerpt from *Annotated Alphabetic List*

SPORTS
I3.450.642.845+
only /class /hist; SPORTS is the activity, SPORTS MEDICINE is the speciality; inj = ATHLETIC INJURIES (& see note there; Manual 30.31)
CATALOG: do not use /pop wks
ATHLETICS was see under SPORTS 1963-75
use SPORTS to search ATHLETICS back thru 1966
see related
    ATHLETIC INJURIES
    DOPING IN SPORTS
X   ATHLETICS
XU   BASEBALL
XU   BICYCLING
XU   GOLF
XU   HOCKEY
XU   SKATING
XU   SOCCER
XU   TENNIS
XU   WEIGHT LIFTING
XU   WRESTLING
XR   EXERTION

SPORTS MEDICINE
G2.403.830
SPEC: SPEC qualif except /methods; differentiate from SPORTS; sports inj = ATHLETIC INJURIES; policy: Manual 30.31

The Tree Structures

The *Tree Structures* is a subject-arranged listing of the terms from the *Annotated Alphabetic List*. The word "tree" refers to the hierarchically-arranged, branch-like structure of the single letter and number assigned to each heading. There are 15 broad subject areas:

A. Anatomical Terms
B. Organisms
C. Diseases
D. Chemicals and Drugs
E. Analytical, Diagnostic and Therapeutic Technics and Equipment
F. Psychiatry and Psychology
G. Biological Sciences
H. Physical Sciences
I. Anthropology, Education, Sociology and Social Phenomena
J. Technology, Industry, Agriculture, Food
K. Humanities
L. Information Science and Communication
M. Named Groups of Persons
N. Health Care
Z. Geographicals

These broad categories are broken down into subcategories, and then narrower and narrower divisions.

The following example from the *Tree Structures* (figure 3.2) shows part of the page where the MeSH term SPORTS is found indented under the progressively broader terms RECREATION, LEISURE ACTIVITIES, and the subcategory HUMAN ACTIVITIES of Category I.

Figure 3.2 Excerpt from *Tree Structures*

I3—HUMAN ACTIVITIES

HUMAN ACTIVITIES (NON MESH)	I3		
ACTIVITIES OF DAILY LIVING	I3.50	E2.831.67	N2.421.784.
AUTOMOBILE DRIVING	I3.125		
AUTOMOBILE DRIVER EXAMINATION	I3.125.299		
DIET FADS	I3.287	E2.924.270	
LEISURE ACTIVITIES	I3.450		
HOLIDAYS	I3.450.345		
RECREATION	I3.450.642		
CAMPING	I3.450.642.159		
DANCING	I3.450.642.287		
HOBBIES	I3.450.642.469		
PLAY AND PLAY-THINGS	I3.450.642.693		
SPORTS	I3.450.642.845		
BASEBALL*	I3.450.642.845.110		
BICYCLING*	I3.450.642.845.140		
BOXING	I3.450.642.845.210		
FOOTBALL	I3.450.642.845.300		
GOLF*	I3.450.642.845.400		
GYMNASTICS	I3.450.642.845.417	I2.233.543.	
HOCKEY*	I3.450.642.845.475		
MOUNTAINEERING	I3.450.642.845.582		
RUNNING	I3.450.642.845.610		
JOGGING*	I3.450.642.845.610.320		
SKATING*	I3.450.642.845.700		
SKIING	I3.450.642.845.775		
SOCCER*	I3.450.642.845.800		
SWIMMING	I3.450.642.845.869		
DIVING	I3.450.642.845.869.110	G3.230.150.	
TENNIS*	I3.450.642.845.900		
TRACK AND FIELD	I3.450.642.845.925		
WEIGHT LIFTING*	I3.450.642.845.950		
WRESTLING*	I3.450.642.845.975		
RELAXATION	I3.450.769		
REST	I3.450.769.647		

*Indicates minor descriptor

Explode Command. The *EXPLODE* command, one of the most important software features of MEDLINE, relates to the *Tree Structures*. EXPLODing makes it possible to "OR" terms indented under a broader tree number as well as the term they are indented under. All terms with a common tree number will be "ORed" together. For example, in figure 3.2, EXPLODing LEISURE ACTIVITIES will perform the following Boolean process, "OR-ing" together all terms that begin with I3.450:

LEISURE ACTIVITIES OR HOLIDAYS OR RECREATION OR CAMP-
ING OR DANCING OR HOBBIES OR PLAY AND PLAYTHINGS OR
SPORTS OR BASEBALL OR BICYCLING OR BOXING OR FOOT-
BALL, etc.

Pre-explosions (Cascades). Large tree explosions requiring excessive computer time have been exploded in advance at NLM (*pre-exploded*) and at DIALOG (*cascaded*). At BRS, all tree numbers have already been pre-exploded. The *Annotated Alphabetic List* contains a list of the pre-explosions found only in NLM's MEDLINE. Each of NLM's pre-explodes is marked with a large black dot in both the *Annotated Alphabetic List* and the *Trees*. The number of pre-explodes increases every year. A list of DIALOG and NLM pre-explodes can be found in Appendix F.

Permuted Medical Subject Headings

The *Permuted Medical Subject Headings* takes each significant word of a MeSH term and lists all the MeSH terms in which that word exists indented under that word. Figure 3.3 shows the MeSH term SPORTS and terms near it alphabetically.

HOW MeSH TERMS ARE CATEGORIZED

In addition to the terms that appear only in *Index Medicus*, other categories of MeSH terms provide multiple access points in MEDLINE.

Major Descriptors. A *major descriptor* is any MeSH term which never appears as a "SEE UNDER" reference. It may appear in *Index Medicus* and can always be searched in MEDLINE. The MeSH terms GILLS and SPORTS in figure 3.4 (page 16) are examples of major descriptors.

Minor Descriptors. A *minor descriptor* is always a "SEE UNDER" to a major descriptor. It can never appear in *Index Medicus* but is always searchable in MEDLINE. VANILLIC ACID, in figure 3.5 (page 17), is an example of a minor descriptor.

Majored MeSH Terms. A *majored MeSH term* represents a major concept in a reference and receives an asterisk during the indexing process at NLM. If the term SPORTS had an asterisk appended to it during indexing (∗SPORTS), it would represent a major aspect or central concept of an article. Before 1975, asterisks could only be appended to major descriptors.

Figure 3.3 Excerpt from *Permuted Medical Subject Headings*

SPORES
SPORES
SPORES, BACTERIAL
SPORES, FUNGAL

SPORIDESMINS
SPORIDESMINS see under **INDOLES**

SPOROTHRIX
SPOROTHRIX see **SPOROTRICHUM**

SPOROTRICHOSIS
SPOROTRICHOSIS

SPOROTRICHUM
SPOROTRICHUM

SPOROZOA
SPOROZOA

SPORTS
DOPING IN SPORTS
DRUG ABUSE, SPORTS see **DOPING IN SPORTS**
SPORTS
SPORTS MEDICINE

SPOT
BLIND SPOT see **OPTIC DISK**

SPOTTED
NEWT, RED-SPOTTED see **NOTOPHTHALMUS VIRIDESCENS**
ROCKY MOUNTAIN SPOTTED FEVER

SPOUSE
SPOUSE ABUSE

SPRAGUE
RATS, SPRAGUE-DAWLEY see **RATS, INBRED STRAINS**

SPRAINS
SPRAINS AND STRAINS

Figure 3.4 Major Descriptors

GILLS①
  A13.421②
  68③

① *Major Descriptor*—term does not appear as a "SEE UNDER" reference.

② *Tree Number*

③ *History Note*—term became a major descriptor in 1968.

SPORTS①
I3.450.642.845+ ②
only /class /hist; SPORTS is the activity, SPORTS MEDICINE is the speciality; inj = ATHLETIC INJURIES (& see note there; Manual 30.31) ③
CATALOG: do not use /pop wks④
ATHLETICS was see under SPORTS 1963–75⑤
use SPORTS to search ATHLETICS back thru 1966⑥
see related
    ATHLETIC INJURIES⑦
    DOPING IN SPORTS
X   ATHLETICS⑧
XU BASEBALL
XU BICYCLING⑨
XU GOLF
XU HOCKEY
XU SKATING
XU SOCCER
XU TENNIS
XU WEIGHT LIFTING
XU WRESTLING
XR EXERTION⑩

① *Major Descriptor*—no dates means that the term has been in the MEDLARS system since 1963 and searchable in MEDLINE since 1966. It does not appear as a "SEE UNDER" reference.

② *Tree Number*—(+) indicates that narrower terms are indented under this number in the *Trees*.

③ *Indexing Annotation*—meant for indexers, but helpful for searchers. Do not follow its instructions to the letter because they often contain more details than a searcher needs.

④ *Cataloging Annotation*—used by catalogers. Cataloging subheadings differ slightly from indexing subheadings.

⑤ *History Note*—ATHLETICS was a "SEE UNDER" reference to SPORTS from 1963–1975.

⑥ *Online Note*—all articles previously indexed to ATHLETICS have been mapped to SPORTS.

⑦ *Forward SEE RELATED References*—leads to two more related headings.

⑧ *Backward SEE Reference*—has been made from ATHLETICS to SPORTS.

⑨ *Backward SEE UNDER References*—BASEBALL, BICYCLING, etc., are all minor descriptors.

⑩ *Backward SEE RELATED Reference*—has been made from EXERTION to SPORTS.

Figure 3.5 Minor Descriptor

VANILLIC ACID①
D2.241.223.106.505.850② D2.241.511.390.850②
D2.755.410.850②
do not use /biosyn /defic /physiol; /analogs
NIM only③
(75); was see under BENZOATES 1968-74④
search BENZOATES 1968-74⑤
see under HYDROXYBENZOIC ACIDS⑥

① *Minor Descriptor*—a "SEE UNDER" to a major descriptor. (See items 4 and 6 below.)

② *Tree Numbers*—term is found in three locations in the *Trees*.

③ *Indexing Annotation*—meant for indexers, but helpful for searchers. Here, several subheadings are forbidden with this term.

④ *History Note*—term became a minor descriptor in 1975. Note the use of parentheses (75) to denote a minor descriptor.

⑤ *Online Note*

⑥ *Forward SEE UNDER Reference*—to major descriptor HYDROXYBENZOIC ACIDS.

Certain routine concepts checked for in each article (CHECK TAGS) (for example, HUMAN, FEMALE, MALE, and geographic MeSH terms such as CANADA or UNITED STATES) can never be preceded by an asterisk and appear in *Index Medicus* even though they are major descriptors.

Mapping. *Mapping* is the automatic addition by computer of an appropriate MeSH term to a record. When an asterisk is appended to a minor descriptor, the appropriate major descriptor is added, or mapped-to, and also asterisked. That asterisked major descriptor will appear in *Index Medicus*. For example, if the minor descriptor VANILLIC ACID (figure 3.5) was the central concept of an article, it would appear as *VANILLIC ACID with the additional asterisked mapped-to major descriptor *HYDROXY-BENZOIC ACIDS. Because of this process, an article dealing with VANILLIC ACID as a major aspect would appear in *Index Medicus* under the MeSH term HYDROXYBENZOIC ACIDS.

Non MeSH Terms. *Non MeSH terms* are used to group subject headings in the *Tree Structures*. They can be EXPLODEd to retrieve the indented MeSH terms under them, but nothing is indexed to them specifically. For example, HUMAN ACTIVITIES (NON MeSH) (figure 3.2) can be EXPLODEd, but there will be nothing indexed to it separately.

Entry Terms and Data Form Abbreviations. *Entry terms* ("SEE" references), *data form abbreviations* (MeSH term abbreviations), and alternate forms are searchable in NLM's MEDLINE due to the automatic online interactions with NLM's MeSH VOCABULARY FILE. Some data form abbreviations are searchable in DIALOG's MEDLINE, but their use is not recommended for complete retrieval. SEE references are not necessarily synonymous, e.g., WEIGHT GAIN "SEE" BODY WEIGHT.

"Indexing Annotations, Abbreviations, and Symbols," a one-page guide in the *Alphabetic Annotated List*, provides the meaning of many of the abbreviations and symbols found in *MeSH*. (See figure 3.6.)

Figure 3.6 Indexing Annotations, Abbreviations, and Symbols

Abbreviation	Meaning
GEN	General only; prefer the specific
SPEC	Specialty only; do not use as a coordinate
SPEC qualif	Use only those subheadings permitted with specialties
IM	Usually IM
NIM	Usually NIM
IM or NIM	Coordinate as IM or NIM depending upon the slant or emphasis of the text
no qualif	No subheading permitted
only /	Use only the subheadings noted
do not use /	Do not use the subheadings noted
TN	*Technical Note* with number cited
/ permitted	All subheadings available to the category are permitted but special reference is made to the permitted subheadings specified by this annotation
Manual	*Indexing Manual* with section cited
+ with number	As 23.26+, a section of the *Indexing Manual* with all dependent subsections, as 23.26.1, 23.26.2, etc.
policy	General indexing policy
Bull	*NLM Technical Bulletin* with number, month, and year cited
DF:	Data Form abbreviation
coord	Coordination or coordinate with
+	Coordinate with
Cat	Category
=	Equals or is synonym for
CATALOG:	Catalogers' notes
/ad-poi-tox	The subheadings /adverse effects /poisoning /toxicity
/blood-csf-urine	The subheadings /blood /cerebrospinal fluid /urine
●	Pre-explosion
84(75)	The dates of terms are chronological from right to left. The left date contains the most complete status of a term. Dates in parentheses apply to minor descriptors.

Adapted from:
The *Annotated Alphabetic List.*

HOW TO FIND THE TERMS YOU ARE SEEKING

A list of sources from which MeSH terms are derived can be found in the "black-and-white" *MeSH*. *Dorland's Illustrated Medical Dictionary*[2] is the dictionary source in this list. It is an excellent place to consult when looking for a term which does not seem to exist in *MeSH*.

Sometimes you will have to look very carefully if you are not familiar with *MeSH*. For example, "bleeding" is found under HEMORRHAGE and related terms, but there is no cross reference from "bleeding." It is also wise to routinely consider the inverted forms of the terms you seek. HEMORRHAGE, GASTROINTESTINAL is used, not "gastrointestinal hemorrhage." The *Permuted MeSH* is a good source to refer to since it lists all the headings in which a significant word exists. For example, the heading AORTOCORONARY BYPASS can easily be discovered by looking in the *Permuted MeSH* under BYPASS.

Searchers must consider alternate forms for the same concept—for example, alternates for the term EYE include OPHTHALMOL-, OPH-THALMIC-, OCULAR, VISION, VISUAL, OPTIC, etc. In addition, interchangeable word fragments within a single word should be considered, for example TRACHEOESOPHAGEAL FISTULA is used rather than "esophagotracheal fistula."

Searchers should also scan above and below the alphabetic location in the *Alphabetic Annotated List* where the term should appear—"immunodeficiency diseases" is found under IMMUNOLOGIC DEFICIENCY SYNDROMES.

Often scanning the *Trees* under a broader term will lead to the location of an elusive, indented term. For example, when looking for "bone pins" under the broader subject heading ORTHOPEDIC EQUIPMENT, the MeSH term BONE NAILS is discovered.

Drugs are listed in *MeSH* under their common or generic names, not the trade or proprietary names used by a manufacturer for a specific product. For example, the drug Valium will be found indexed with the nonproprietary name DIAZEPAM.

HOW TO USE PREVIOUS INDEXING INSTRUCTIONS

The "New Medical Subject Headings with Previous Indexing" section is found in each year's edition of *MeSH*. It contains a list of new MeSH terms with no directly corresponding headings. When a new MeSH term appears that simply replaces another one with a directly corresponding heading—as with T LYMPHOCYTES which replaced T-LYMPHOCYTES—previous indexing instructions are not necessary. Examples of new 1984 MeSH terms with no directly corresponding headings follow, with instructions for searchers about the way they were most likely indexed in the past.

NEW HEADING	PREVIOUSLY-INDEXED-UNDER HEADING
*AORTOPULMONARY SEPTAL DEFECT	AORTA/abnormalities (66-83) AORTA, THORACIC/abnormalities (66-83) HEART DEFECTS, CONGENITAL (66-83) PULMONARY ARTERY/abnormalities (66-83)
COLONIC POLYPS	COLONIC NEOPLASMS (66-83) INTESTINAL POLYPS (66-83)
ELDER ABUSE	AGED (66-83) CRIME (68-83) VIOLENCE (68-83)
FLUSHING	(No previously-indexed instructions)
*WOMEN, WORKING	WOMEN (66-83)

Here, an asterisk means minor descriptor.
Adapted from: New Medical Subject Headings with Previous Indexing, 1984

When searching for a new heading in the years prior to its inclusion in *MeSH*, use common sense. The previously-indexed-under instructions provide the framework for retrospective searching; but, as you can see from the representative examples, these instructions can be too broad, too detailed, or non-existent.

One note of caution: do not routinely "AND" all the previously-indexed-under headings. Various combinations will usually be best. Few will work out as neatly as "ANDing" COLONIC NEOPLASMS to INTESTINAL POLYPS to produce COLONIC POLYPS.

Often, textwords must be used in conjunction with MeSH terms to make retrieval more precise. Every article on WOMEN will not be relevant if you are searching for "working women." When no indexing instructions are given, as in the example FLUSHING, searchers should consider as many textwords and MeSH terms as possible: FLUSH—, FLASH—, VASODILATION, etc. Sometimes MeSH terms that have been used in the past to index a new MeSH term have not been included in previously-indexed-under instructions. Previously-indexed-under instructions are also found in NLM's online MeSH VOCABULARY FILE. The meaning and scope of each new MeSH heading appears in *MeSH* each year.

HOW TO USE CORRECT SUBHEADINGS

Subheadings are the 76 subdivisions of MeSH terms that group together important concepts. Several lists of subheadings are available in *Medical Subject Headings, Annotated Alphabetic List.*

The meaning and scope of each subheading appears in "Topical Subheadings with Scope Notes and Allowable Categories." See Appendix G. Allowable categories designate which tree numbers are applicable with a specific subheading.

immunology (A-D, F3)
Used for immunologic studies of tissues, organs, microorganisms, fungi, viruses, and animals; includes immunologic aspects of diseases but not immunologic procedures used for diagnostic, preventive, or therapeutic purposes, for which 'diagnosis,' 'prevention & control,' or 'therapy' are used. Also used for chemicals as antigens or haptens.

The dates upon which subheadings first entered the system, indexing and searching abbreviations, and allowable categories appear in the "Alphabetic List of Topical Subheadings with Abbreviations, Allowable Categories, and Year of Entry Since 1966." See Appendix H. An annotated sample entry follows:

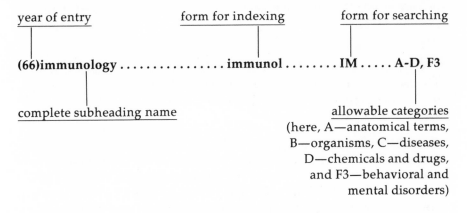

year of entry   form for indexing   form for searching

(66)immunology .... immunol .... IM ..... A-D, F3

complete subheading name   allowable categories
(here, A—anatomical terms,
B—organisms, C—diseases,
D—chemicals and drugs,
and F3—behavioral and
mental disorders)

Subheadings are also arranged by allowable tree category in "Topical Subheadings by Category, Abbreviations and Year of Entry (1) Since 1975 (2) 1966-74" found in the *MeSH Annotated Alphabetic List.* (See Appendix I for a complete list of these subheadings since 1975.) For example, you can look in Category C — DISEASES and see that there are 40 allowable subheadings for anatomical MeSH terms ranging from AN (ANALYSIS) and IM (IMMUNOLOGY) to VE (VETERINARY).

INDEXING PRINCIPLES AND THEIR RELATION TO MEDLINE SEARCHING

NLM has developed a set of principles to index the material in the MEDLARS system. These rules are described in great detail in the *MED-LARS Indexing Manual, Part II.* Although MEDLINE can be searched without any knowledge of its indexing principles, a large percentage of relevant articles may be missed.

Eleven of the most important indexing principles follow. Searching applications are included when appropriate.

The most specific MeSH term is used. An article on a specific concept is indexed to the specific concept, not to a more general one, unless the article discusses *both* the specific and the general topic. For example, an article on acne will be indexed to the MeSH term ACNE, not SKIN DISEASES. General subject headings, such as SKIN DISEASES, are reserved for general articles on skin diseases, those that deal with a large number of skin diseases, or those that deal with a skin disease which does not have its own MeSH term.

Concepts which have no exact MeSH equivalent are indexed to the most closely-related existing MeSH term. Thus, seminal vesiculitis is indexed under SEMINAL VESICLES, while nurses' caps are indexed to CLOTHING. Concepts with the prefixes pre-, post-, pseudo-, and the suffixes -oid and -like are usually found under the most specific equivalent MeSH term. For example, pseudoappendicitis is indexed to APPENDICITIS, and gout-like to GOUT.

Negative findings are indexed as if they were positive findings. A drug believed to lessen the symptoms of rheumatoid arthritis, but that has been found not to be effective, is indexed to ARTHRITIS, RHEUMATOID/ DRUG THERAPY.

MeSH terms in the form of -OLOGY and -IATR- generally refer to the practitioner, the field, or the specialty. An article about the personalities of endocrinologists will be indexed to the specialty term ENDOCRINOL-OGY, not to ENDOCRINE DISEASES or ENDOCRINE GLANDS. Specialty terms will have the annotation *"SPEC:SPEC qualif"* meaning these are specialty terms and therefore only those subheadings permitted with specialties can be used. The list of these subheadings is found in the introduction to the *Annotated MeSH.*

The most precise description of a concept is often expressed by combining ("coordinating") two or more MeSH terms or using a MeSH term/subheading combination. Indexers use combined terms to express a concept when a pre-combined subject heading does not exist.

LEVEL	FORM	MeSH STRATEGY
Most specific	Pre-combined MeSH term	BRAIN NEOPLASMS CHILD PSYCHOLOGY
Less specific	MeSH term/subheading	BRAIN/DRUG EFFECTS ARTHRITIS/PSYCHOLOGY
Least specific	Organ MeSH term and related MeSH term	RETINAL VEIN AND RETINAL DISEASES GLOTTIS AND LARYNGITIS
Least specific	Two or more unrelated MeSH terms	HYPERTENSION AND ADOLESCENCE MATHEMATICS AND ANXIETY

A disease heading is always considered to be more specific than an organ heading. The disease "jejunitis" does not have a MeSH term. It will be indexed under the disease JEJUNAL DISEASES (rather than JEJUNUM) and ENTERITIS.

For complete retrieval when searching for all aspects of an organ or an organ disease, search for the organ terms "ORed" with the organ disease terms and any other related terms. To retrieve everything on the kidney, a searcher would EXPLODE KIDNEY "ORed" with EXPLODE KIDNEY DISEASES "ORed" with KIDNEY FUNCTION TESTS, RENAL CIRCULATION, etc.

Neoplasms are indexed under the site—in the form of an organ neoplasm heading—and a histologic type. "Adenocarcinoma of the colon" would be indexed as COLONIC NEOPLASMS (site) and ADENOCARCINOMA (histologic type).

If an organ neoplasm heading does not exist in *MeSH*, it is indexed under the closest organ neoplasm heading, the organ, and the histologic type. For example, "basal cell carcinoma of the thumb" is indexed under HAND NEOPLASMS, THUMB, and BASAL CELL CARCINOMA. *MeSH* makes no distinction between malignant and benign tumors.

The importance of a MeSH term is indicated by "weighting." MeSH terms can be assigned as *Index Medicus headings (IM)* or *non-Index Medicus headings (NIM)*. An IM heading means that the term can appear in *Index Medicus* and represent the central or major point of an article. NIM headings are usually retrieved through MEDLINE. Both types of headings are always searchable in MEDLINE; searchers can limit the number of references to be retrieved to major IM concepts.

Some MeSH terms will never be IM. HUMAN is one example, yet there are a vast number of references indexed to it. Often techniques and routine concepts are NIM because they simply limit or describe something else, e.g., RETROSPECTIVE STUDIES (NIM) "AND" LEGIONNAIRE'S DIS-
✓ EASE (IM), or ELECTROCARDIOGRAPHY (NIM) "AND" MYOCARDIAL INFARCTION (IM).

Each article is indexed in enough depth to retrieve it from multiple access points within the confines of MeSH indexing principles. Articles from journals assigned as Priority 1 or 2 are usually indexed in greater depth than Priority 3 journals. NLM expects searchers to enhance their retrieval with textwords when comprehensiveness is needed. Information which is merely mentioned but not actually discussed, such as routine electroen-cephalographic studies in neurologic diseases, will not be assigned a MeSH term for the technique. To retrieve everything on this technique, a MEDLINE searcher would need to search for textwords such as EEG, EEGS, ELECTROENCEPHALOGRAPH-, etc., "ORed" with the MeSH term ELEC-TROENCEPHALOGRAPHY.

Some relational concepts cannot be indexed with precision using MeSH terms. Degrees of quality or quantity, such as good, best, less, partial, or total, are not searchable with MeSH terms. Neither are very specific time relation-ships, such as before, after, early, or often (except as TIME FACTORS, or LONGITUDINAL STUDIES, or RECURRENCE, etc.). The concepts of primary or secondary (except for the subheading SECONDARY for neo-plasms) and body positions (such as above, below, right, or left [except for LATERALITY and CEREBRAL DOMINANCE]) are also hard to express using only MeSH terms. MEDLINE searchers must use textwords when dealing with the types of concepts mentioned above. For example, the concept "one-lung" anesthesia requires the use of the textword ONE next to LUNG.

Large-volume concepts are routinely "checked" for in each article by indexers and are called as check tags. Check tags reliably pinpoint specific age groups, males or females, humans or animals, review articles, case reports, etc. Check tags are especially important in clinical medicine since patient characteristics are essential concepts when specific patient populations are described. A list of these check tags appears in figure 3.7.

Detailed definitions of check tags are given in the *Indexing Manual.* An article on a newborn infant is indexed under HUMAN and under INFANT, NEWBORN. MEDLINE searchers only need to search INFANT, NEWBORN. Check tags make it possible to reliably limit search retrieval to common parameters.

The check tags for age apply only to humans; MALE and FEMALE apply to either humans or animals. HUMAN will not be used for articles dealing with obviously human concepts such as medical schools, politics, or social welfare.

Figure 3.7 Check Tags

Human	Current Biog-Obit
Animal	
Male	Historical Article
Female	Historical Biography
Pregnancy	History of Medicine, Ancient
In Vitro	History of Medicine, Medieval
Case Report	History of Medicine, Modern
Comparative Study	
Review	History of Medicine, 15th Cent.
English Abstract	History of Medicine, 16th Cent.
Monograph	History of Medicine, 17th Cent.
	History of Medicine, 18th Cent.
Infant, Newborn (birth to 1 month)	History of Medicine, 19th Cent.
Infant (1 month to 23 months)	History of Medicine, 20th Cent.
Child, Preschool (2–5 years)	
Child (6–12 years)	Support, Non-U.S. Gov't
Adolescence (13–18 years)	Support, U.S. Gov't, Non-P.H.S.
Adult (19–44 years)	Support, U.S. Gov't, P.H.S.
Middle Age (45–64 years)	
Aged (65 years and over)	

Cats
Cattle
Chick Embryo
Dogs
Guinea Pigs
Hamsters
Mice
Rabbits
Rats

Subheadings group together important aspects of MeSH terms. As discussed earlier in this chapter, there are currently 76 subheadings listed in three different ways in MeSH. (See Appendices G, H, and I.)

Be careful not to limit your search immediately to MeSH term/subheading combinations. Sometimes the combination of several MeSH terms will narrow your strategy sufficiently, and further limitation by subheadings would be too restrictive. Use subheadings when they are needed to specify particular aspects of a topic. An example of this situation is mammography *causing* breast cancer. Without the use of subheadings, you would retrieve everything on mammography used diagnostically in breast cancer.

Knowing when to use subheadings and which ones to use takes some practice. NLM has produced a suggested guide which groups subheadings in subject arrangements. See Appendix J. *Note: you cannot EXPLODE subheadings.*

For example, if you need to express the therapy of a disease, you can consider using some or all of the following subheadings: THERAPY, DIET THERAPY, DRUG THERAPY, NURSING, PREVENTION & CONTROL, RADIOTHERAPY, REHABILITATION, SURGERY, and TRANSPLANTATION; for the adverse effects of a substance, always use: ADVERSE EFFECTS, POISONING, and TOXICITY; for the analysis of a substance, consider: ANALYSIS, BLOOD, URINE, and CEREBROSPINAL FLUID.

Certain subheading relationships are so common in indexing that NLM includes a list of them in their MEDLINE training program. See Appendix K: Subheadings—Common Combinations.

The subheading METABOLISM can be used to express many metabolic concepts. Information also taken from NLM's training sessions about this subheading appears in Appendix L.

The use of *free-floating subheadings*—subheadings searched without attachment to a MeSH term—is discussed in Chapter Four under "Subheadings."

RELIABILITY OF MEDLINE INDEXING

How reliable is MEDLINE indexing? A recent article by Funk and Reid[3] looked at the consistency of indexing in 760 twice-indexed journal articles. It showed that check tags had the highest consistency overall. Central concept MeSH terms and subheadings were applied more consistently than peripheral concepts. Free-floating subheadings were applied more consistently than MeSH terms with attached subheadings.

These findings should encourage MEDLINE searchers to use as many search terms as necessary when comprehensive search retrieval is needed. There is no single correct way to index an article or to retrieve it.

References
[1]Wos M. MESHin' around. Milwaukee: 1984.
[2]Dorland's illustrated medical dictionary. 26th ed. Philadelphia: Saunders, 1981.
[3]Funk ME, Reid C. Indexing consistency in MEDLINE. Bull Med Libr Assoc 1983 Apr; 71:176–83.

Chapter Four

Software Features

This chapter describes selected aspects of search software, some of which are unique to the MEDLINE database. For instructions about logging in, changing files, printing references online or offline, downloading, and saving or storing search strategies, etc., refer to the detailed instructions in the appropriate system manual.

The first section in this chapter describes general software features. The second section deals with methods for searching important MEDLINE fields (described in Chapter Two) using BRS, DIALOG, and NLM and discusses software features unique to MEDLINE.

GENERAL FEATURES

BRS, DIALOG, and NLM employ different methods of performing search operations. During the online process, searchers issue software commands in various ways depending upon the vendor.

Default and Qualification

There are various *defaults*—options assumed when none are specified—built into online search systems. Knowledge of system defaults helps the experienced searcher save online time and the new searcher make fewer search errors when too many options are available. The first default is to the database you are connected to each time you log in. In BRS, you must specify which database you want. In DIALOG, default is to ERIC (the education database). In NLM, the default is to the most recent segment of MEDLINE.

Which fields are searched when none are specified is a very important default feature. The same term typed into MEDLINE on each of the three systems can give you different numbers of *postings*—numbers of items indexed to the term.

In the BRS system, when entering an *unqualified term*, one that has not been limited to certain fields, the default is to terms in all searchable fields in its *dictionary file*. BRS, DIALOG, and NLM have variously named and kinds of alphabetical indexes of searchable terms. They are: dictionary file (BRS), basic index (DIALOG), and index file (NLM).

To override the default when searching on a term, the term requires *qualification*—a limitation to a certain field or fields. Qualification of terms is shown in the following examples for BRS.

BRS:

PAIN	This is an unqualified term. It retrieves the MeSH term PAIN, the textword, the author's address term, the single-word journal title abbreviation, and any occurrence of PAIN in any other field.
PAIN.DE.	This retrieves PAIN as a MeSH term. The qualifier is the two-letter field designator for MeSH terms—DE—separated from the term by a period on either side. In BRS, qualifiers can be distinguished from two-letter subheading abbreviations by the use of two periods.
PAIN.TI,AB.	This retrieves PAIN as textword by the use of the field qualifiers TI (title) and AB (abstract). The comma separates the fields.
PAIN.IN.	This retrieves PAIN as a term from the author affiliation—IN—field.

In the BRS system, all multi-word MeSH terms are hyphenated (for example, BRAIN-CHEMISTRY), and apostrophes in MeSH terms are omitted (BURKITTS-LYMPHOMA).

DIALOG's default for unqualified terms in the basic index is to textwords, MeSH terms, enzyme numbers and the name of substance which the EC number identifies, the name of substance which the CAS registry number identifies, check tags, and named persons. (These default fields are not in any order of priority.)

Some other fields are also searched with a prefix and are not part of the basic index of DIALOG. For example, six check tags are searchable as *DOCUMENT TYPE* with the prefix DT= . They are: REVIEW, MONOGRAPH, ENGLISH ABSTRACT, CURRENT BIOG-OBIT, HISTORICAL ARTICLE, and HISTORICAL BIBLIOGRAPHY.

In the DIALOG system, each set of terms should be preceded by the letters "SS" for *SELECT STEPS*. The select steps approach gives each term a separate search statement number.

The following examples demonstrate how default works using DIALOG.

DIALOG:

SS PAIN

This is an unqualified term. It retrieves the MeSH term PAIN and the textword PAIN.

SS PAIN/DE

This retrieves PAIN as a MeSH term. The qualifier is the two-letter field designator for MeSH terms—DE—separated from the term by a slash. In DIALOG, qualifiers are distinguished from two-letter subheading abbreviations by the slash mark.

SS PAIN/TI,AB

This retrieves the term PAIN as a textword by the use of the field qualifiers TI (title) and AB (abstract). A comma separates the fields.

SS CS=PAIN

This retrieves PAIN as a term in the CS (corporate source) field. This field is in a separate index and is searched with a prefix equals (=) sign.

NLM's default when entering an unqualified term is to all directly searchable fields (authors, MeSH terms, etc.) *except* textwords, journal title abbreviations, journal codes, name of substance, pre-explosions, and *name fragments* (of the name of substance). The following examples demonstrate the use of NLM's default.

NLM:

PAIN

This retrieves PAIN as a MeSH term only.

PAIN(TW)

This retrieves PAIN as a textword by the use of the field qualifier TW—textword—separated from the term by parentheses. Only one qualifier can be attached to a term when directly searching like this.

ALL PAIN   This retrieves PAIN as a MeSH
term, a textword, and as a single-
word journal title abbreviation.
Note the *"ALL"* command to override the default and search for
everything in the basic index.
"ALL" will also override NLM's
MULTI-MEANING MESSAGE
which occurs when a term appears
in the basic index in more than one
field or form.

Boolean Operators

Boolean logic was described in the first chapter. The following examples
demonstrate how sets or terms (in this case, INFLUENZA and COUGH)
can be combined in various relationship using BRS, DIALOG, and NLM.

The "AND" operator:

BRS:
INFLUENZA AND COUGH

DIALOG:
SS INFLUENZA AND COUGH

NLM:
INFLUENZA AND COUGH

The "OR" operator:

BRS:
INFLUENZA OR COUGH

DIALOG:
SS INFLUENZA OR COUGH

NLM:
INFLUENZA OR COUGH

Note: Sometimes "ANDs" and "ORs" get confused. For example, a searcher
looking for "vitamin E and danazol in the treatment of fibrocystic breast
disease" probably wants articles on *either* "vitamin E *or* danazol," not the
two together as would be indicated by the "and."

Note: Embedded "ANDs" in multi-word MeSH terms must be disguised by replacing one of the characters in DIALOG and NLM. For example, to search for the multi-word MeSH term STAINS AND STAINING:

DIALOG:

SS STAINS 'AND' STAINING	Single or double quotation marks can be used.

NLM:

STAINS A#D STAINING	The hash mark (#) stands for one character.

Since multi-word MeSH terms are hyphenated in the BRS system, embedded "ANDs" are already disguised.

The "NOT" operator:

BRS:
INFLUENZA NOT COUGH

DIALOG:
SS INFLUENZA NOT COUGH

NLM:
INFLUENZA AND NOT COUGH

Note: Beware of the "NOT" strategy when subject searching. For example, when searching for "aspirin studies done only in humans" it is better to search for ASPIRIN "AND" HUMAN rather than ASPIRIN "NOT" ANIMAL. The latter strategy will lose articles indexed to both ANIMAL *and* HUMAN. Consider using the NOT strategy to delete previous search statements that have already been printed and seen.

When you have more than one kind of logical operator in a single search statement, the "ANDs" are processed before the "ORs." The only way to override this logic is to use parentheses, or *nesting*, which will perform the operations within the parentheses first. Note, however, that nesting is not available from NLM.

The following examples demonstrate the order of Boolean operators. Sets are created by the groups of records on each line, and are numbered for clear sequence.

BRS:
1. STRESS AND COFFEE OR TEA
This is equivalent to (STRESS AND COFFEE) OR TEA.
2. STRESS AND (COFFEE OR TEA)
Nesting overrides the natural Boolean order of operators.

DIALOG:
1. SS STRESS AND COFFEE OR TEA
This is equivalent to SS (STRESS AND COFFEE) OR TEA.
2. SS STRESS AND (COFFEE OR TEA)
Nesting overrides the natural Boolean order of operators.

NLM:
1. STRESS AND COFFEE OR TEA
This is equivalent to (STRESS AND COFFEE) OR TEA.
2. STRESS
3. COFFEE OR TEA
4. 2 AND 3
Search statement 4 is equivalent to STRESS AND (COFFEE OR TEA).

Truncation

Truncation is the process of allowing for alternate endings or beginnings of a word stem to appear without having to specify what those endings or beginnings will be. For example, truncation allows for NEUROLOGIC, NEUROLOGICAL, NEUROLOGIST, NEUROLOGISTS, NEUROLOGY, etc. Though not technically truncation, allowing for embedded variable internal characters is referred to as internal truncation.

For BRS, the truncation symbol is a dollar sign ($); there is no internal truncation. Left-hand truncation will appear in the new BRS/SEARCH software.

BRS:

ADENOMA$ This retrieves the stem ADENOMA with up to 100 entries in the dictionary file beginning with that term.

SMITH-J$ This retrieves the author SMITH J with up to 100 entries in the dictionary file beginning with that stem. Note in BRS, authors' last names and initials are hyphenated and bound.

CONSIST$2   This retrieves the stem CONSIST with as many as two additional characters at the end.

DIALOG's truncation symbol is a question mark (?); there is internal truncation, but the ? must stand for something.

DIALOG:

SS ADENOMA?

This retrieves the stem ADENOMA with up to 1000 entries in the basic index beginning with ADENOMA.

SS AU=SMITH J?

This retrieves the author SMITH J with up to 1000 entries in the additional author index beginning with this stem.

SS CONSIST?? ?

This will retrieve the stem CONSIST with up to two additional characters following it. The two question marks (??) specify the number of possible additional characters.

SS WOM?N

This will retrieve WOMAN or WOMEN. Each question mark used internally represents one variable character.

For NLM, the colon (:) stands for any number of characters as well as no characters. The pound sign or hash mark (#) stands for only one character or space; it cannot replace the lack of any character or space.

NLM:

ALL ADENOMA:

This retrieves the stem ADENOMA with up to 450 entries in the index file beginning with that term. ALL is used to avoid the MULTI-MEANING MESSAGE.

ALL SMITH J:

This retrieves the author SMITH J with up to 450 entries in the index file beginning with that stem. ALL is used to avoid the MULTI-MEANING MESSAGE.

ALL CONSIST##

This retrieves the stem CONSIST with up to two additional characters at the end. ALL is used to avoid the MULTI-MEANING MESSAGE.

ALL WOM#N

This will retrieve WOMAN or WOMEN. The internal # mark represents a variable character. ALL is used to avoid the MULTI-MEANING MESSAGE.

ALL TUMO:R:

This will retrieve TUMOR, TUMOUR, TUMOURS, TUMORS, etc. The internal colon represents a variable character or no character. This internal truncation feature is unique to NLM.

Positional Operators and Stringsearching

Positional operators are special operators used besides the standard Boolean operators "AND," "OR," and "NOT" to indicate more precise relationships between certain terms in a reference. For example, in the following search situations the use of positional operators is appropriate: employing the adjacency of terms in the phrase "low risk" or looking for the words "males" and "lupus" in the same sentence of an article.

Both BRS and DIALOG have positional operators.

In NLM, you cannot directly search for the position of terms. You must first retrieve terms with postings, and then *STRINGSEARCH* them—scanning the resulting strings of characters in these references for a desired relationship expressed by a proximity of terms.

Important, detailed information about positional operators can be found in the BRS and DIALOG users' manuals. Instructions about the string-search command can be found in the NLM manual.

The following example shows the use of positional operators to search for the textword phrase "low-risk" or "low risk." The BRS operator to use is ADJ—adjacency for terms side by side and in that order. The DIALOG operator to use is (W)—adjacency of terms side by side, and in that order.

BRS:
LOW ADJ RISK

LOW and RISK must appear side by side and in that order. Note the use of the ADJ operator.

DIALOG:
SS LOW(W)RISK

LOW and RISK must appear side by side and in that order. Note the use of the (W) operator.

In DIALOG you can specify how many words can intervene between terms by including that number with the W; for example, SS

LOW(2W)RISK would retrieve up to two intervening words—"low levels of risk," etc. (See DIALOG textword generation rule 2 in the textword section of this chapter.)

NLM:

1. (TW) LOW AND RISK

Note the use of TW (textword) qualifying the set of terms. LOW and RISK are searched for as textwords first to create a set with postings.

2. TS :LOW#RISK: OR :LOW#RISK:(AB)

Stringsearching of search statement 1 is performed by using the TS (stringsearch) command which scans the string of characters in the title and abstract (AB) fields. The default in stringsearching in MEDLINE is to title, so you don't have to specify TI (title) for the first "low#risk." (The default in string-searching may be different in other NLM databases.) Hash marks (#) are included in case "low" and "risk" are hyphenated in the actual title or abstract.

Stringsearching, only available through NLM, scans each field separately. *Stringsearching scans the oldest records in a set first.* Before you stringsearch, try to create the smallest set possible because stringsearching is a time-consuming process. NLM recommends stringsearching as a time-saving procedure especially when the retrieval is to be less than 300 postings. Stringsearching has advantages in some search situations because it can be used for fields not directly searchable such as titles or pagination. It can also be used for left-hand truncation, for stopwords not directly searchable, and for heavily-posted terms. In most cases, use colons on either side of a term, unless only one form of a term exists such as ENG for English language articles, or HUMAN for human studies. The NLM users' manual goes into greater depth on stringsearching and should be consulted for important details. The following example shows the use of stringsearching for heavily posted terms.

NLM:

1. PNEUMONIA, MYCOPLASMA	A set is created.
2. TS (LA) ENG AND HUMAN(MH)	The set in search statement 1 is stringsearched first in the LA (language) field and then in the MH (MeSH term) field. Colons are not needed because only one form exists for each term in this case.

To stringsearch on a search statement other than the previous one with postings, include the search statement number in the command. In the following example, you are at search statement 5 and are stringsearching the retrieval of a previously created set in search statement 1. You are looking for the check tags INFANT; INFANT, NEWBORN; CHILD; CHILD, PRESCHOOL; and ADOLESCENCE which are in the MH (MeSH term) field. (These check tags cover the ages from birth to 18 years.) The use of colons retrieves both INFANT and both CHILD check tags. *You cannot stringsearch on MeSH terms having commas (e.g., INFANT, NEWBORN) by leaving the commas in place. They must be changed to colons or truncated early.*

NLM:
5. TS 1 (MH) :INFANT: OR :CHILD: OR :ADOLESCENCE:

HOW VENDORS HANDLE IMPORTANT MEDLINE FIELDS

The following examples show how to search the MEDLINE fields described in Chapter Two using BRS, DIALOG, and NLM. They also include software features unique to MEDLINE such as the EXPLODE command.

Abstracts

Words in an Abstract. To search for the word "velocity" in an abstract:

BRS:

VELOCITY.AB.	VELOCITY qualified to the AB (abstract) field.

DIALOG:

SS VELOCITY/AB	VELOCITY qualified to the AB (abstract) field.

NLM:

1. VELOCITY(TW)   VELOCITY is retrieved in the TW
                                       (textword) field.

2. TS :VELOCITY: (AB)   As abstract words cannot be di-
                                       rectly searched for, the stringsearch
                                       command (TS) is used to search for
                                       VELOCITY in the AB (abstract)
                                       field from search statement 1.

English Abstracts for Foreign Language Articles. To search for articles
about GUILT in foreign language articles having English abstracts either
online or only with the printed article:

BRS:

GUILT AND   GUILT is limited by "ANDing" it
ENGLISH-ABSTRACT   with the check tag ENGLISH-
                                       ABSTRACT.

DIALOG:

SS GUILT AND DT=ENGLISH   GUILT is limited by "ANDing" it
ABSTRACT   with the prefix DT= (document
                                       type) field for English abstract.

NLM:

GUILT AND ENGLISH   GUILT is limited by "ANDing" it
ABSTRACT   to the check tag ENGLISH
                                       ABSTRACT.

Online Abstracts. To search for GUILT in English and non-English
language articles having an online abstract:

BRS:

GUILT AND AUTHOR.AB.   All abstracts available online have
                                       AUTHOR in the AB (abstract au-
                                       thor) field.

DIALOG:

SS GUILT AND AB=ABSTRACT   All abstracts available online are
                                       designated by AB=ABSTRACT.

NLM:

GUILT AND AUTHOR(AA)   All abstracts available online have
                                       AUTHOR in the AA (abstract au-
                                       thor) field.

Authors

Because of the possible variations in authors' names, it is often best to use truncation symbols after a first initial to retrieve all forms. To search for an uncommon author name such as Harold E. Lebovitz:

BRS:
LEBOVITZ-H$ In BRS, all authors' names and ini-
                                   tials are hyphenated. They are
                                   searched as a bound unit.

DIALOG:
SS AU=LEBOVITZ H?   AU specifies author.

NLM:
ALL LEBOVITZ H: The ALL command will override
                                   the MULTI-MEANING MESSAGE,
                                   if the author's initials or other des-
                                   ignations appear in more than one
                                   way.

Because of possible variations in entry, it will sometimes be necessary to scan entries above and below a desired name in the same way you would glance at the index to a book. Three different names for this "scanning" command are used by the three vendors: BRS—*ROOT*, DIALOG—*EXPAND*, and NLM—*NEIGHBOR*. These commands can be used in any field. Check your user manuals for more information. To scan the entries above and below H. Lebovitz:

BRS:
ROOT LEBOVITZ-H   Authors' names are hyphenated
                                   and searched as a bound unit.

DIALOG:
E AU=LEBOVITZ H   E specifies expand.

NLM:
NBR LEBOVITZ H   NBR specifies neighbor.

Authors' Addresses

For NLM searchers, the author's address field is found only in NLM's SDILINE file which contains the latest month's MEDLINE references. This field cannot be directly searched at NLM; it must be stringsearched from a previously created set of references. Therefore, BRS (which has author's address back to 1977) and DIALOG (which has this field back to 1982) should be used instead.

Because of the lack of standardization in an author's address, MEDLINE searchers using BRS or DIALOG need to include all possible variations in spelling. In the examples below, to search for articles published by researchers at Humana Hospitals in the State of Kentucky, it is necessary to include the abbreviation KY as well as KENTUCKY.

BRS:

HUMANA.IN. AND (KY OR   IN specifies author affiliation.
KENTUCKY).IN.

DIALOG:

CS=HUMANA AND (CS=KY   CS specifies corporate source.
OR CS=KENTUCKY)

To search for a "common name" (R.SMITH) when an organizational affiliation (Duke) is known:

BRS:
SMITH-R$ AND DUKE.IN.

DIALOG:
SS AU=SMITH R? AND
CS=DUKE

NLM
FILE SDILINE   The NLM strategy can use only one
                          month of MEDLINE references, so
                          retrieval is very limited.

1. ALL SMITH R:
2. TS (AD) :DUKE: AD specifies address.

Journal Subsets

To search for references on the Olympics from *Abridged Index Medicus* (AIM) journals only:

BRS:
OLYMPIC$ AND A.SB.   A.SB. specifies the AIM subset.

DIALOG:
SS OLYMPIC? AND SF=AIM   SF=AIM specifies the AIM subset.

NLM:
ALL OLYMPIC: AND A(SB)   A(SB) specifies the AIM subset.

DIALOG searchers cannot limit their searches to Priority 1 and 2 journals. To search for references on the OLYMPICS only from Priority 1 and 2 journals through BRS and NLM:

BRS:
OLYMPIC$ AND M.SB.   M.SB. specifies Priority 1 and 2 journals.

NLM:
ALL OLYMPIC: AND M(SB)   M(SB) specifies Priority 1 and 2 journals.

Languages

English language. To limit references on LIPID BILAYERS to English:

BRS:
1. LIPID-BILAYERS
2. ..L/1 LG=EN   BRS commands are preceded by two dots (..); L stands for limit. LG stands for language and EN specifies English.

DIALOG:
SS LIPID BILAYERS NOT   This is the only way to limit re-
**   LA=NONENGLISH**   trieval to English language articles in DIALOG.

NLM:
LIPID BILAYERS AND NOT   FOR(LA) stands for foreign lan-
**   FOR(LA)**   guage articles.
        or

LIPID BILAYERS AND ENG(LA)   ENG(LA) specifies English language articles. The first NLM approach is more cost-effective because you are matching a smaller percentage of the records (approximately 24%) against LIPID BILAYERS.

Non-English Languages. To limit references on LIPID BILAYERS to French language articles:

BRS:
LIPID-BILAYERS AND LGFR   Language names appear with the LG label followed immediately by the two-letter abbreviation.

DIALOG:
SS LIPID BILAYERS AND   Language names are spelled out in
  LA=FRENCH   full.

NLM:
LIPID BILAYERS AND FRE(LA)   Language names are three-letter
                                   abbreviations.

Check vendor manuals for abbreviations or forms for non-English languages on the system you are using.

Monographs

To search only for monographs in MEDLINE:

BRS:
MONOGRAPH.DE.   DE specifies MeSH term.

DIALOG:
SS DT=MONOGRAPH   DT calls for document type.

NLM:
MONOGRAPH

Registry Numbers and Enzyme Numbers

When you use CAS registry or EC numbers to search, it is still important to include textwords and sometimes even broader MeSH terms to retrieve references prior to June 1980, or the date they entered the MEDLARS system.

See Appendix E for a description of *Medical Subject Headings—Supplementary Chemical Records* used to obtain terms for chemical searching. For example, to search for Fuller's Earth, one could include its registry number "ORed" with the textwords FULLER "AND" EARTH "ORed" with the textword FLORIDIN. (In BRS, FULLER'S becomes FULLERS; see discussion of textword generation rules.)

To search only for the CAS registry number for Fuller's Earth (8031-18-3):

BRS:
8031-18-3

DIALOG:
SS RN=8031-18-3   In DIALOG, registry numbers are
                        searchable with the prefix RN= .

NLM:
8031-18-3

To search only for the EC number for GDPmannose dehydrogenase (EC 1.1.1.132):

BRS:
EC-1-1-1-132

DIALOG:
SS EC 1.1.1.132   In DIALOG, EC numbers (unlike CAS numbers) are in the basic index and are directly searchable.

NLM:
EC 1.1.1.132

Source

Individual components of this field—the abbreviated journal title, year, month, volume, issue, and pages of a reference—can be searched. However, not all components are searchable at each vendor. Refer to vendor manuals for more information.

Searching by page numbers can be very useful when completing a partial citation. This feature is available through BRS and NLM. To search for an article by R. Smith in the *New England Journal of Medicine,* pages 192-8, when no volume number or year is known:

BRS:
SMITH-R$ AND NEW-ENGL-J-MED
** AND 192-8**

NLM:
1. ALL SMITH R: AND NEW   TA stands for journal title abbrevia-
** ENGL J MED(TA)**   tion.
2. TS (PG) :192-8   PG stands for pagination.

Special List Indicators

Before 1975, Special List journals were not indexed as completely as the other Index Medicus *journals. Check tags and majored MeSH terms were not assigned.* Searches that limit a dental or nursing topic by check tags or majored subject headings will lose all articles appearing in special list journals before 1975. Even today, special list journals may not have any subject headings relating to that specialty. Therefore, use special list journals as subject concepts or terms to be "ORed" with other related terms.

To search for the subheading NU (NURSING) "ORed" with the special list nursing journals:

BRS:
NU OR N.LI.   N.LI. specifies special list nursing.

DIALOG:
SS NU OR SF=NURSING   SF=NURSING specifies special list nursing.

NLM:
NU OR N(LI)   N(LI) specifies special list nursing.

Subject Headings

Indexers assign MeSH terms, or majored subject headings, to MEDLINE references. Subject headings can have subheadings attached to them.

To search for the MeSH term DYSLEXIA, ACQUIRED:

BRS:
DYSLEXIA-ACQUIRED   In BRS, all multi-word headings are hyphenated.

DIALOG:
SS DYSLEXIA, ACQUIRED

NLM:
DYSLEXIA, ACQUIRED

MeSH terms are *double posted* in the BRS and DIALOG systems. This means that any individual word in a multi-word MeSH term can be directly searched. NURSING in BRS and DIALOG will also retrieve EDUCATION, NURSING; SURGICAL NURSING; etc. Double posting unlocks multi-word MeSH terms and makes it easier to find a concept you are looking for if it is embedded.

As discussed previously, the weighting (importance) of a MeSH term is indicated by whether it may appear in *Index Medicus* as an IM heading or major concept of a reference, asterisked during the indexing process, or as a non-*Index Medicus* (NIM) heading. Usually three or four MeSH terms per reference will be asterisked, while a reference will have, on the average, 8–10 subject headings plus check tags.

To search for the MeSH term MASSAGE as the major aspect of a reference:

BRS:
MASSAGE.MJ.   MJ calls for a major MeSH term.

DIALOG:
SS MASSAGE/DE*   DE* calls for a major MeSH term.
        or
1. SS MASSAGE
2. LIMIT1/MAJ

NLM:
***MASSAGE**

MeSH terms also can be used with the EXPLODE command, pre-explosions, and subheadings. Detailed descriptions of these features follow.

Explosions
This important software capability provides for the time-saving Boolean "ORing" of indented MeSH terms under a specific tree number as well as the term they are indented under. It makes it possible to search large numbers of headings in a single command, and to retrieve all levels of specificity of a concept.

The following examples demonstrate the use of the EXPLODE command for VENOMS (D24.185.965):

BRS:
EX D24.185.965$ In BRS, either the EX or EXP commands for EXPLODE can be used. You must truncate the tree number.

DIALOG:
SS DC=D24.185.965?   In DIALOG, DC= (descriptor code) is used with the tree number. You must truncate the tree number.

NLM:
EXP VENOMS   In NLM, either the heading itself
        or   or the tree number can be used.
EXP D24.185.965   EXP specifies EXPLODE.

To search for the "majored" exploded VENOMS (D24.185.965):

BRS:
EX D24.185.965$.MJ.   MJ specifies MAJOR.

DIALOG:
1. SS DC=D24.185.965?
2. LIMIT1/MAJ   MAJ specifies MAJOR.

NLM:

EXP *VENOMS
or
EXP *D24.185.965

In NLM, either the heading or the tree number can be used. The asterisk (*) specifies MAJOR.

When you "AND" EXPLODEd terms against other explosions or other MeSH terms, be sure the same tree number does not appear on each side of the "ANDed" combination. In that case, you will retrieve *everything* on the term with the common tree number, for you have literally "ANDed" it against itself; for example, a search on the ophthalmologic aspects of Sjogren's syndrome "ANDs" EXPLODEd C11 (EYE DISEASES) against C11.496.719 (SJOGREN'S SYNDROME). Every reference to Sjogren's syndrome will be retrieved with this logic.

When using explosions for a term having more than one tree number with a plus sign (+) after it, always check each tree number because there can be different terms indented under the numbers in different locations in the trees. THORAX is one example of a MeSH term with different terms indented under it at its two tree locations. In the *Alphabetic Annotated List* it appears as:

THORAX
A1.911+   A2.835.232.904+

In the *Trees* it appears in Category A-Anatomical Terms with the following indented MeSH terms in the A1-Body Regions and in the A2-Musculoskeletal System subcategories.

THORAX	A1.911
MEDIASTINUM	A1.911.529
THORAX	A2.835.232.904
RIBS	A2.835.232.904.567
STERNUM	A2.835.232.904.766
MANUBRIUM*	A2.835.232.904.766.442
XIPHOID BONE*	A2.835.232.904.766.825

Pre-explosions

Pre-explosions (see Appendix F) must be searched for differently from "regular" explosions. The following examples demonstrate this for the MeSH terms indented under ANTIBIOTICS (D20.85).

BRS:

EX D20.85$

In BRS, all tree numbers are already pre-exploded, so the process is identical to EXPLODE.

DIALOG:
SS DC=D20.85.   Pre-explosions end with a period
                                     rather than a question mark as in
                                     explosions.

NLM:
ANTIBIOTICS(PX)   In NLM, the name of the pre-ex-
                                     plode must be used, not the tree
                                     number. The qualifier PX in par-
                                     entheses (pre-explosion) is used.
                                     Do not confuse it with the PX
                                     subheading for psychology; qual-
                                     ifiers are in parentheses.

Subheadings

The 76 subheadings are listed in Appendices G, H, and I. A subheading
can be searched in different ways: attached singly or multiply to MeSH
terms, or "free-floating"—in which the MeSH term to which it is attached
is not specified. Entering a MeSH term alone retrieves that heading with *all*
its subheadings attached automatically. For example, searching for the
MeSH term BRAIN is also the same as searching for BRAIN/ABNORMALI-
TIES, BRAIN/ANATOMY & HISTOLOGY, BRAIN/DRUG EFFECTS, etc.

Single Subheadings. The following examples demonstrate the use of
single subheadings attached to MeSH terms for three topics: CHEMICAL-
LY-INDUCED (CI) REYES SYNDROME; CHEMICALLY-INDUCED (CI)
REYES SYNDROME or PEPTIC ULCER; and SKIN DISEASES, INFEC-
TIOUS (C17.838) MORTALITY (MO).

BRS:
1. REYES-SYNDROME-CI   In BRS, subheadings cannot be
                                     spelled out. Note that REYE'S be-
                                     comes REYES.

2. QS (REYES-SYNDROME OR   QS is a *QUICKSEARCH* command
**   PEPTIC-ULCER) WITH CI**   used to attach subheadings to sin-
                                     gle MeSH terms (not EXPLODEd
                                     terms) to save computer processing
                                     time.

3. EX C17.838$ WITH MO

DIALOG:

1. SS REYE'S SYNDROME(L)CI   Subheadings can be spelled out or
                                   abbreviated. The L operator links
                                   MeSH terms with attached sub-
                                   headings.

2. SS REYE'S SYNDROME(L)CI   Nesting around the L operator is
   OR PEPTIC ULCER(L)CI   not yet available. In *DIALOG Ver-
                                   sion 2*, an enhanced version of pres-
                                   ent DIALOG software, this will be
                                   possible.

3. SS DC=C17.838?(L)MO

NLM:

1. REYE'S SYNDROME/CI   Subheadings can be spelled out or
                                   abbreviated; the slash mark at-
                                   taches subheadings to a MeSH
                                   term.

2. SUBS APPLY CI   In NLM, the SUBS APPLY com-
   REYE'S SYNDROME OR   mand applies one or more subhead-
   PEPTIC ULCER   ings to all search statements with
   SUBS CANCEL   MeSH terms following the com-
                                   mand. The SUBS CANCEL com-
                                   mand must be used to stop the
                                   application of subheadings to
                                   subsequent search statements.

3. EXP C17.838/MO   Either a tree number or a MeSH
        or   term can be EXPLODEd.
   EXP SKIN DISEASES,
   INFECTIOUS/MO

Multiple Subheadings. The examples that follow demonstrate the use
of multiple subheadings attached to MeSH terms. The first search statement shows the subheading abbreviations for ADVERSE EFFECTS (AE),
TOXICITY (TO), and POISONING (PO) attached to the MeSH term
DIAZEPAM. The second search statement shows the subheadings ADMIN-
ISTRATION & DOSAGE (AD) and THERAPEUTIC USE (TU) attached to
the EXPLODEd MeSH term ANTICONVULSANTS (D14.261).

BRS:

1. QS DIAZEPAM WITH
   (AE TO PO)
2. EX D14.261$ WITH (AD TU)   The WITH operator attaches a sub-
                                   heading to a MeSH term.

DIALOG:
1. **SS DIAZEPAM(L)AE OR**
   DIAZEPAM(L)TO OR
   DIAZEPAM(L)PO
2. **SS DC=D14.261?(L)AD OR**
   DC=D14.261?(L)TU

For both DIALOG examples, multiple subheadings cannot be nested. With DIALOG Version 2, this will be possible. For example, the first DIALOG search statement above will look like: SS DIAZEPAM(L) (AE OR 'TO' OR PO).

NLM:
1. **SUBS APPLY AE, TO, PO**
   DIAZEPAM
   SUBS CANCEL
2. **SUBS APPLY AD, TU**   You can also EXPLODE the tree
   EXP ANTICONVULSANTS   number for anticonvulsants
   SUBS CANCEL   (D14.261).

Free-Floating Subheadings. Use free-floating subheadings when a desired MeSH term/subheading combination is not allowed or when a broad concept can be expressed by a subheading. Free-floating subheadings will increase retrieval. For example, a search involving all types of injuries should include the free-floating subheading INJURIES (IN) "ORed" with the pre-explode WOUNDS AND INJURIES.

The following examples show the use of the free-floating subheading MORTALITY (MO) "ANDed" to EXPLODED LIVER (A3.620) with the subheading TRANSPLANTATION (TR) to search for "liver transplantation mortality."

BRS:
EX A3.620$ WITH TR AND   DE specifies MeSH term.
MO.DE.

DIALOG:
SS DC=A3.620?(L)TR AND MO

NLM:
EXP LIVER/TR AND MO

The previous strategies will retrieve articles with the subheading MORTALITY (MO) attached to MeSH terms such as INTRAOPERATIVE COMPLICATIONS, POSTOPERATIVE COMPLICATIONS, LIVER DISEASES, and IMMUNOLOGIC DEFICIENCY SYNDROMES. The use of the free-floating subheading saves the searcher having to express all the possible ways that MO could be attached to a MeSH term.

Free-floating subheadings can also be made the central concept. In the following examples, the subheading TRANSPLANTATION (TR) is used:

BRS:
TR.MJ.   MJ specifies major.

DIALOG:
SS TR/DE*   DE* specifies major.
    or
1. SS TR
2. L1/MAJ

In NLM, you cannot directly search for a free-floating subheading. You must stringsearch the retrieval in a previous search statement. In the following example, a previously-created set (search statement 1, not shown) is stringsearched for TRANSPLANTATION (TR) as a central concept.

NLM:
2. TS (MH) :*TR :   MH (MeSH term) is the qualifier to
                                                      use here.

Stringsearching for majored subheadings can be very time-consuming if there are more than 300 postings for the previously-created set to be stringsearched. It is much easier to go to BRS or DIALOG if you have these choices available.

Pre-explosions and Subheadings. When using NLM, note that sub-headings cannot be directly attached to pre-explodes. Therefore, when you need to use subheadings attached to a pre-explosion, either search for the pre-explosion as an explosion and directly attach the desired subheading or "AND" a subheading to the pre-explosion. In the following examples, the pharmacodynamics (PD) of all antibiotics is being searched. (ANTIBI-OTICS is a pre-explode.)

NLM:
EXP ANTIBIOTICS/PD
    or
ANTIBIOTICS(PX) AND PD   (PX) is the qualifier for pre-ex-
                                                plode. This strategy will retrieve
                                                more references.

Textwords

As discussed in Chapter Two, textwords are computer-generated and "text-edited" depending on the specific rules of the vendor. A short description of these textword generation rules follows. In general, all special characters, such as commas, periods, colons, are converted to blanks. For more detailed information, consult your vendor manuals. Because of the possible variations in the entry of textwords, it is important to use the ROOT, EXPAND, and NEIGHBOR commands.

BRS:
1. The apostrophe before an "s" ('s) is ignored. For example, SOCIETY'S becomes SOCIETYS.
2. Hyphenated character strings are retained under certain conditions. Strings with up to three alphabetic characters on the left followed by a hyphen and at least one numeric on the right are retained with the hyphen, e.g., LD-50. Strings with at least one numeric on the left followed by a hyphen, followed by only one alphabetic character on the right also retain their hyphens, e.g., 14-C remains as 14-C and not two separate textwords 14 and C. Also, 2,4,5-T remains as 2,4,5-T. (Commas in this numeric string are retained.)

DIALOG:
1. All special characters are converted to blanks.
2. When using adjacency, stopwords must be taken into account. The expression "right to know," is searched in the DIALOG system as RIGHT(1W)KNOW since "to" is a stopword and must be taken into account.
3. "A" is not a stopword.

NLM:
1. Numbers composed of all numerics, e.g., 21 or 101, are stopwords. You can only stringsearch for them. (However, 21st is not a stopword because it is composed of a numeric and letters.)
2. See BRS rule 2 on hyphenation.
3. A hyphen is inserted between numeric strings and a single alphabetic character, e.g., 14C becomes 14-C.

Regardless of the system you use, when searching for a textword composed of numeric and alphabetic characters, try it hyphenated, with a space, as one word, and in reverse order, e.g., 14-C, 14 C, 14C, C14, etc.

To search for the textword "velocity":

BRS:
VELOCITY.TI,AB.   TI specifies title, AB specifies abstract.

DIALOG:
SS VELOCITY/TI,AB   TI specifies title, AB specifies abstract.

NLM:
VELOCITY(TW)   TW specifies textword.

Titles

Individual words in titles are searchable based on the textword generation rules discussed in the previous paragraphs.
To search only for the title word "velocity":

BRS:
VELOCITY.TI.   TI specifies title.

DIALOG:
SS VELOCITY/TI   TI specifies title.

NLM:
1. VELOCITY(TW)   In NLM, title and abstract words
2. TS :VELOCITY: cannot be directly searched. You must use the stringsearch command. TW specifies textword. TS is the stringsearch command. Since the default in MEDLINE in stringsearching is to title, there is no need to qualify to title in search statement 2.

Years

The year a reference was published in MEDLINE is searchable. For example, to search for all articles on FERRETS published in 1984:

BRS:
FERRETS AND YR84
        or
1. FERRETS
2. ..L/1 YR=84

DIALOG:
SS FERRETS AND PY=1984   PY specifies publication year.

NLM:
FERRETS AND 84(YR)
        or
1. FERRETS
2. TS :84: (DP)   DP calls for date of publication.

To search for all articles on FERRETS published in 1983 or 1984:

BRS:
FERRETS AND (YR83 OR YR84)
    or
1. FERRETS
2. ..L/1 YR>82   > specifies greater than.

DIALOG:
SS FERRETS AND
  PY=1983:PY=1984

NLM:
1. FERRETS
2. 1 AND 83(YR)
3. 1 AND 84(YR)
4. 2 OR 3
    or
1. FERRETS
2. TS (DP) :83: OR :84:

Chapter Five

Search Strategy Formulation

Previous chapters have covered the basic elements of MEDLINE—MeSH terms, subheadings, explosions, textwords, check tags, etc. This chapter on search strategy formulation merges these elements. Several processes are involved: breaking down a search topic into its component parts, deciding how precise and how comprehensive your retrieval should be, performing a search interview if you are running the search for someone else, constructing basic search strategies, and using common search techniques.

HOW TO BREAK THE SEARCH TOPIC INTO ITS COMPONENTS

To analyze a search topic you must first conceptualize it, breaking it down into its component parts. To do this, write what is needed in your own words. It is more efficient to translate something concrete into MeSH terms and textwords than to force an unwritten idea into the written language of MEDLINE. Because MEDLINE charges begin as soon as you go online, it is also practical to prepare your search first on paper, unless your search topic is very simple.

Include all possible component parts in your conceptualization. Decide whether the search topic should be limited to certain age groups, human or animal subjects, males or females, languages, years, reviews, etc.

Some searchers underline, draw Venn diagrams, bracket, or circle parts of a search request. Others make lists of the concepts to be searched.

DETERMINING RETRIEVAL PRECISENESS AND COMPREHENSIVENESS

The same search topic often can be formulated in MEDLINE in different ways to obtain either precise or more comprehensive results depending upon your needs. The concepts of precision and recall deal with the percentage of relevant articles retrieved.

The precision ratio for MEDLINE retrieval is defined as:

$$\frac{\text{number of relevant references retrieved}}{\text{all references retrieved}}$$

The recall ratio for MEDLINE retrieval is defined as:

$$\frac{\text{number of relevant references retrieved}}{\text{all relevant references contained in MEDLINE}}$$

Sometimes you will have a very high precision ratio—that is, a large percentage of your retrieved references will be relevant. However, the actual recall ratio—how many of the total number of relevant references in MEDLINE on your topic were retrieved—may be low. You must decide which kind of retrieval ratio you need for each search topic, and then use appropriate search strategies.

For example, when writing a grant proposal you probably will prefer a comprehensive search with a high recall ratio. However, in an emergency patient-care situation, in which you need just a few good references, you most likely will want to run a search with a high precision ratio. In the latter case, using textwords rather than MeSH terms may be appropriate.

PERFORMING A SEARCH INTERVIEW

If you are running a search for someone else, the search interview is an integral part of the search process.[1] When conducting a search interview, be sure you understand the real topic of the search, the reason it is being run, the number of references expected, the number of references desired, the years to be covered, the restrictions to humans or animals, etc., and cost limitations, if any. In addition, ask if a relevant reference is already known. Have the person for whom you are running a search write down what he or she is looking for. Search request forms can make this task easier.

HOW TO CONSTRUCT SEARCH STRATEGIES

There are three main ways to construct search strategies: the "building block" approach, the reference "pearl growing" approach, and the limiting of a concept through successive fractions. Often searchers will use combinations of all of them.

The Building Block Approach

With this approach, an information request is divided into subsets or blocks and then the blocks are combined. For example:

(computed tomography or nuclear magnetic resonance) and the chest

opthalmologic manifestations of orthopedic diseases

Sometimes one of the subsets is so specific that it can be searched by itself, especially if little has been written about it. For example, the effects of chicken soup on the respiratory tract can be searched for as chicken soup (CHICKEN "AND" SOUP) because so little has been written about chicken soup in the medical literature. Lawn mower accidents can be searched as MOWER (truncated) because there will be so little in MEDLINE about mowers.

If one block in a search strategy seems very specific, search for it first. If you retrieve too many references, then add one or more of the other blocks.

Sometimes combining several blocks will result in a small retrieval or none at all. Instead, try combining fewer blocks. For example: if the search strategy for the concept stress and swine and diabetes mellitus produces nothing, try stress and swine, or try stress and diabetes mellitus and animals.

Reference Pearl Growing

In this type of search strategy construction, you use the most specific terms of your request to retrieve a relevant article. Then the indexing terms for this article are reviewed online and may often be used to construct a search strategy to retrieve similar articles. This process may be repeated several times with the indexing terms of the new articles retrieved.

For example, to do a comprehensive search for "Baby Doe"-type cases, use the textwords "baby" and "doe." Then locate a good reference or two, and look at the indexing—ABNORMALITIES; INFANT, NEWBORN; LEG-ISLATION, MEDICAL; HANDICAPPED; EUTHANASIA, PASSIVE, etc.— to construct a search strategy to complement your textword search.

Limiting a Concept Through Successive Fractions

This strategy is used when you are interested in a broad subject area but must narrow down the subject to make it manageable. For example, you wish to obtain recent articles on sodium, but when you get online you realize that there are too many articles not dealing with what you really want—SODIUM "AND" POTASSIUM. You still get too many articles, so you "AND" in another parameter of your request—EXPLODEd HOR-MONES. When you still retrieve too many articles, you limit the retrieval further to English-language articles and humans:

1. SODIUM   (4881 references)
2. 1 AND POTASSIUM   (1969 references)
3. 2 AND EXPLODE HORMONES   (308 references)
4. 3 AND ENGLISH AND HUMAN   (122 references)

USING COMMON SEARCH TECHNIQUES

The following search techniques can be used to provide flexibility in MEDLINE strategies. An experienced MEDLINE searcher will often use combinations of them.

Postqualification

The technique of *postqualification* takes previous search results and restricts them to certain fields. This technique can play a large role in cost-effective *iterative* searching in MEDLINE. In iterative searching, you change or modify a search strategy because of something learned while online.

Postqualification saves time because you do not have to re-enter the same terms repeatedly. In BRS you can postqualify to any field except to an "ANDed" search statement. With DIALOG, you can postqualify to an "ANDed" statement, majored MeSH terms, human and animal references, and accession numbers. In NLM postqualification is not available.

In the following examples, the postqualification techniques have been italicized.

BRS:
1. CALCIUM
2. *1.MJ.*   MJ specifies majored MeSH terms.
3. *1.TI.*   TI specifies title.
4. 1 AND HUMAN
5. BIOFEEDBACK AND
   HYPERTENSION
6. BIOFEEDBACK.MJ. AND
   HYPERTENSION.MJ.

DIALOG:
1. SS CALCIUM
2. *LIMIT1/MAJ*   L can be used instead of LIMIT.
3. SS CALCIUM/TI
4. *LIMIT1/HUMAN*
5. SS BIOFEEDBACK AND
   HYPERTENSION
6. *LIMIT 5/MAJ*

NLM:
1. CALCIUM
2. *CALCIUM
3. TS 1 :CALCIUM:
4. 1 AND HUMAN
5. BIOFEEDBACK AND
   HYPERTENSION
6. *BIOFEEDBACK AND
   *HYPERTENSION

Increasing Recall

When you increase recall you retrieve a greater number of the relevant references on your topic in MEDLINE. The following techniques demonstrate how to do this.

EXPLODE MeSH terms to retrieve all levels of specificity of a concept. For example, you will retrieve more eye diseases by EXPLODing EYE DISEASES than by searching for the single, general heading EYE DISEASES.

Use correct MeSH terms, especially when a subject heading has been changed.

Begin your search with unweighted MeSH terms. Don't automatically make MeSH terms major.

"AND" fewer concepts together so that there will be fewer conditions to be satisfied.

When using textwords, employ as many synonyms as possible. Also, be aware of variant spellings—singular, plural, adjectival, British and American,[2] and typographical errors. Typographical errors will often appear for commonly misspelled words such as "hemorrhage" and "ophthalmology." Be sure to truncate textwords when appropriate. For example, don't limitlessly truncate CAT if you only want CAT or CATS. If you do, you will also retrieve CATASTROPHE, CATIONS, and CATTLE. If you want to retrieve everything in MEDLINE on "Chinese restaurant syndrome" truncate the word "restaurant" to retrieve "restaurants" as well.

When using textwords, do not automatically use proximity operators or search on "variable" textwords. For example, if you are searching for the Fontan procedure, also known as the Fontan method and the Fontan operation, etc., it is best to simply use the textword "Fontan." Omit the variable textwords for "procedure." When you want to use two or more textwords, for example, "bilateral tenderness," the use of adjacency operators specifying both textwords side by side would eliminate appropriate references such as "bilateral and unilateral tenderness."

When using a MeSH term, also use its equivalent in textwords. For example, HYPERALDOSTERONISM is a MeSH term. Searching for it as both a subject heading and a textword will increase the number of retrieved references to it.

Print MeSH terms and CAS registry numbers from relevant articles to pick up new search strategy ideas. Also print abstracts from relevant articles when appropriate.

Do not routinely use MeSH term/subheading combinations when you begin searching. When subheadings are appropriate, consider using "free-floating" ones. Sometimes you can limit yourself too much by attaching subheadings to specific MeSH terms.

Increasing Preciseness

When you make your retrieval more precise, a larger percentage of your retrieved references will be relevant. The following examples demonstrate techniques for increasing your precision ratio.

Make all or some of the MeSH terms major. For example, there are several methods of combining the MeSH terms CALCIUM and MYOCARDIUM, each yielding a different number of references.

1. CALCIUM AND MYOCARDIUM   **(1981 references)**
2. CALCIUM MAJORED AND MYOCARDIUM
   MAJORED   **(619 references)**
3. CALCIUM MAJORED AND MYOCARDIUM   **(966 references)**
4. CALCIUM AND MYOCARDIUM MAJORED   **(1076 references)**
5. 3 OR 4   **(1423 references)**

The first method has the broadest approach; the second is the narrowest. The fifth method is broader than the second, and preferable when it is not certain that *both* CALCIUM and MYOCARDIUM should be majored.

When searching only with textwords, or using MeSH terms in combination with textwords, limit textwords to the title of the reference. Adjacency of multiword textwords provides further precision. For example, if you are looking for low dose heparin therapy and want to "AND" HEPARIN (with the subheadings ADMINISTRATION & DOSAGE [AD] or THERAPEUTIC USE [TU]) with the textwords "low" and "dose" adjacent to each other, consider the textwords limited to title.

BRS:

QS HEPARIN WITH (AD TU)   QS specifies QUICKSEARCH.
    AND LOW ADJ DOSE.TI.

DIALOG:

SS (HEPARIN(L)AD OR   The operator L links a MeSH term
    HEPARIN(L)TU) AND   and a subheading.
    LOW(W)DOSE/TI

NLM:

1. **SUBS APPLY AD, TU**
   HEPARIN
   SUBS CANCEL
2. **ALL LOW AND ALL DOSE**   The ALL command searches for
   AND 1   everything in the index file, in this
                                     case, textwords.

3. TS :LOW#DOSE:

TS specifies stringsearch. The default in stringsearching is to title, so there is no need to qualify search statement 3. The # mark accounts for the possibility of an intervening punctuation mark.

Limit retrieval to specific journals or journal subsets. You can store a list of journals relevant to your needs, or you can limit your retrieval as the occasion arises.

BRS:
1. **SPORTS-MEDICINE AND (N-ENGL-J-MED OR AM-J-MED)**
2. **ACYCLOVIR AND A.SB.**

A.SB. is the *Abridged Index Medicus* subset.

DIALOG:
1. **SS SPORTS MEDICINE AND (JN=N ENGL J MED OR JN=AM J MED)**

JN specifies journal title abbreviation.

2. **SS ACYCLOVIR AND SF=AIM**

SF=AIM is the *Abridged Index Medicus* subset.

NLM:
1. **(TA) N ENGL J MED OR AM J MED**

TA specifies journal title abbreviation.

2. **1 AND SPORTS MEDICINE**
3. **ACYCLOVIR AND A(SB)**

A(SB) is the *Abridged Index Medicus* subset.

Limit retrieval to specific authors. Note that authors' names are truncated in the three systems. For example:

BRS:
THYROID-NEOPLASMS AND (LEIGHT-G$ OR WELLS-S$)

DIALOG:
SS THYROID NEOPLASMS AND (AU=LEIGHT G? OR AU=WELLS S?)

NLM:
1. **ALL WELLS S: OR ALL LEIGHT G:**
2. **1 AND THYROID NEOPLASMS**

Use subheadings to express which aspect of a MeSH term is desired.

Limit by check tags when necessary.

Limit by language.

Limit by date.

Use CAS registry numbers or EC numbers to search for substances indexed to broader, less-specific MeSH terms.

References

[1]Kolner SJ. Improving the MEDLARS search interview: A checklist approach. Bull Med Libr Assoc 1981 Jan;69:26–33.

[2]Chivers R. Variant English spellings and textword searching. NLM Tech Bull 1976 May;85:5–6.

Chapter Six

Sample Search Strategies

This chapter contains sample MEDLINE searches for six topics using the regular BRS, DIALOG, and NLM systems.

The search strategies include: using Boolean logic, using explosions to retrieve all levels of specificity in *MeSH*, using textwords to discover correct MeSH terms, using subheadings, and limiting retrieval by language, humans, age, major concepts, year, subject-related journals, and textwords.

There is no single "correct" way to run a MEDLINE search; therefore, these search strategies are suggestions only—they are by no means comprehensive.

The searches incorporate the examples from the preceding chapters. However, these examples may look slightly different due to the actual mechanics of the search process. For instance, each system prompts you and indicates postings—the number of items listed for a term or combination of terms—in different ways. This is demonstrated in the following example of a search for the textword MOOSE.

BRS:

1-:	**MOOSE**	-: is the user prompt.
RESULT	**23**	

DIALOG:

? SS MOOSE   ? is the user prompt.

   1   23 MOOSE

NLM:

SS 1 /C?   SS # /C? is the readiness cue mes-

USER: sage SEARCH STATEMENT NUM-

ALL MOOSE   BER OR COMMAND. It is always

                         followed by the user prompt USER.

PROG: PROG stands for program response.

SS (1) PSTG (23)   PSTG represents postings.

Each system only recognizes your input when it is followed by a carriage return.

To print these articles in a standard format, you would type the following:

BRS:
. . P 1 BIBL/DOC=ALL   Commands are entered with two dots.

DIALOG:
T1/3/1-23

NLM:
PRT

Please consult your vendor manuals for more information.

SEARCH 1: LIMITING A TOPIC THROUGH SUCCESSIVE FRACTIONS

Search Topic

All types of calcium channel blockers. Human studies only. English language references only. Recent articles to be limited to the year 1984 if there are more than 200 references. Major aspects only.

Solution

This search strategy shows the successive fractions approach—limiting a large topic until it becomes manageable. The MeSH term CALCIUM CHANNEL BLOCKERS (D18.192) is EXPLODEd to retrieve itself and the indented terms under it. Then these references are further limited by the check tag HUMAN and English language articles. Since there are still too many references, the results are limited further by the 1984 year of publication. Finally, the EXPLODEd CALCIUM CHANNEL BLOCKERS is MAJORED.

Hint

It is easier to start broader, and major the headings later when you know how many articles are retrieved with your search strategy.

Search Comments

BRS search statement 5—Three more articles are found through BRS than through the other two systems because the word HUMAN is retrieving both MeSH terms and textwords.

NLM search statement 2—The time overflow message, TIME OVFLW: CONT? (Y/N), indicates that a procedure requires more computer time than allotted in one "slice" of time. You must type Y if you want the computer to keep processing your search statement.

Search statement 6—PRT COMPR prints fields having more than one item of information run into the same line instead of using a line for each item. In this case, authors appear in the compressed format.

Search 1

BRS:

1-:   EX D18.192$
RESULT   4622
2-:   1 AND HUMAN
RESULT   2641
3-:   ..L/2 LG=EN
RESULT   1839
BRS – SEARCH MODE – ENTER QUERY
4-:   3 AND YR84
RESULT   222
5-:   1.MJ. AND 4
RESULT   178
6-:   ..P 5 BIBL/DOC=1-2

1
AU Bogaert-M-G.   Rosseel-M-T.   Joos-R.   Boelaert-J.
TI Plasma concentrations of nifedipine in patients with renal failure.
SO Arzneimittelforsch.   1984.   34(3).   P 307–8.

2
AU Gielsdorf-W.   Settlage-J-A.   Jaeger-H.
TI Quantitative determination of bencyclane in human plasma by
    capillary gas chromatography/chemical ionization mass
    spectrometry.
SO Arzneimittelforsch.   1984.   34(3).   P 290–2.

END OF DOCUMENTS

DIALOG:

? SS DC=D18.192?
            1   4300 DC=D18.192?
? L1/HUMAN
            2   2444 1/HUMAN
? SS S2 NOT LA=NONENGLISH
            3   354880 LA=NONENGLISH
            4   1717   2 NOT 3
? SS S4 AND PY=1984
            5   92820   PY=1984
            6   219   4 AND 5
? L1/MAJ
            7   3054 1/MAJ
? C6AND7
            8   175 6 AND 7
? T8/3/1-2

(Dialog Search 1, cont.)
8/3/1
1391596   84231596
  Plasma concentrations of nifedipine in patients with renal failure.
  Bogaert MG; Rosseel MT; Joos R; Boelaert J
  Heymans Institute of Pharmacology, University of Gent Medical
    School, Belgium.
  Arzneimittelforsch (GERMANY, WEST), 1984, 34(3) p307-8, ISSN
    0004-4172 Journal Code: 91U

8/3/2
1391592   84231592
  Quantitative determination of bencyclane in human plasma by
    capillary gas chromatography/chemical ionization mass
    spectrometry.
  Gielsdorf W; Settlage JA; Jaeger H
  L.A.B. GmbH, Neu-Ulm, FR Germany.
  Arzneimittelforsch (GERMANY, WEST), 1984, 34(3) p290-2, ISSN
    0004-4172 Journal Code: 91U

NLM:

SS 1 /C?
USER:
EXP CALCIUM CHANNEL BLOCKERS
PROG:
SS (1) PSTG (2839)

SS 2 /C?
USER:
1 AND HUMAN
PROG:
TIME OVFLW: CONT? (Y/N)

USER:
Y
PROG:
TIME OVFLW: CONT? (Y/N)

USER:
Y
PROG:
SS (2) PSTG (1610)

(NLM Search 1, cont.)

SS 3 /C?
USER:
2 AND NOT FOR (LA)
PROG:
SS (3) PSTG (1222)

SS 4 /C?
USER:
3 AND 84(YR)
PROG:
SS (4) PSTG (219)

SS 5 /C?
USER:
EXP *CALCIUM CHANNEL BLOCKERS AND 4
PROG:
SS (5) PSTG (175)

SS 6 /C?
USER:
PRT COMPR 2
PROG:

1
AU – Bogaert MG; Rosseel MT; Joos R; Boelaert J
 TI – Plasma concentrations of nifedipine in patients with renal
       failure.
SO – Arzneimittelforsch 1984;34(3):307–8

2
AU – Gielsdorf W; Settlage JA; Jaeger H
 TI – Quantitative determination of bencyclane in human plasma by
       capillary gas chromatography/chemical ionization mass
       spectrometry.
SO – Arzneimittelforsch 1984;34(3):290–2

SEARCH 2: USING TEXTWORDS TO FIND OUT THE MeSH TERMS USED IN INDEXING

Search Topic
How are kidney stones indexed in MEDLINE?

Solution
If you cannot find a term in *MeSH* for "kidney stones," search with textwords in MEDLINE, then print the MeSH terms used to index relevant-looking references.

Hint
To increase the precision ratio, use adjacency and limit the results to words in titles. (Note the greater number of articles indexed to KIDNEY CALCULI than to the textwords KIDNEY and STONE truncated.)

Search Comments
BRS search statement 2—The majored MeSH terms print out first in the DE (MeSH term) field.

After "END OF DOCUMENTS"—If all possible documents are not printed, BRS remains in the print mode. To revert to the search mode, you enter the command ..S after the user prompt -:

NLM search statement 1—The default in stringsearching is to title, so that there is no need to qualify the terms.

Search 2

BRS:
1-:   KIDNEY ADJ STONE$1
RESULT   127
2-:   1.TI.
RESULT   61
3-:   ..P 2 TI,DE/DOC=1-3

1
TI Percutaneous nephrolithotripsy. An advancement in kidney stone extraction.
DE KIDNEY-CALCULI: su.
   CASE-REPORT. HUMAN. MALE. MIDDLE-AGE. SURGERY-OPERATIVE: mt,td. SURGICAL-NURSING.

(BRS Search 2, cont.)

2

TI Percutaneous ultrasonic lithotripsy (PUL): kidney stone
disintegration.

DE KIDNEY-CALCULI: th.   ULTRASONIC-THERAPY: mt.
URETERAL-CALCULI: th.
CATHETERIZATION.   DILATATION.   HUMAN.   ULTRASONIC-
THERAPY: is. UROGRAPHY.

3

TI Ultrasonic destruction of kidney stones.

DE KIDNEY-CALCULI: th.   ULTRASONIC-THERAPY.
ADULT.   CASE-REPORT.   FEMALE.   HUMAN.   KIDNEY-
CALCULI: ra. MALE.   ULTRASONIC-THERAPY: ae, is.
URETERAL-CALCULI: ra, th.   UROGRAPHY.

END OF DOCUMENTS

-:   ..S

BRS – SEARCH MODE – ENTER QUERY
3-:   KIDNEY-CALCULI
RESULT   1627

DIALOG:

? SS KIDNEY(W)STONE?
            1   109 KIDNEY(W)STONE?
? SS KIDNEY(W)STONE?/TI
            2   52 KIDNEY(W)STONE?/TI
? T2/8/1-3
2/8/1
1390049   84230049
    Percutaneous nephrolithotripsy. An advancement in kidney stone
    extraction.
    Tags: Case Report; Human; Male
    Descriptors: *Kidney Calculi—Surgery (SU); Middle Age; Surgery,
    Operative—Methods (MT); Surgery, Operative—Trends (TD);
    Surgical Nursing

2/8/2
1388094   84228094
    Percutaneous ultrasonic lithotripsy (PUL): kidney stone
    disintegration.
    Tags: Human
    Descriptors: Catheterization; Dilatation; *Kidney Calculi—Therapy
    (TH); Ultrasonic Therapy—Instrumentation (IS); *Ultrasonic
    Therapy—Methods (MT); *Ureteral Calculi—Therapy (TH);
    Urography

(DIALOG Search 2, cont.)
2/8/3
1386071   84226071
  Ultrasonic destruction of kidney stones.
  Tags: Case Report; Female; Human; Male
  Descriptors: Adult; Kidney Calculi—Radiography (RA); *Kidney
    Calculi—Therapy (TH); *Ultrasonic Therapy; Ultrasonic
    Therapy—Adverse Effects (AE); Ultrasonic Therapy—
    Instrumentation (IS); Ureteral Calculi—Radiography (RA); Ureteral
    Calculi—Therapy (TH); Urography

? SS KIDNEY CALCULI
          3   1383 KIDNEY CALCULI

NLM:
SS 1 /C?
USER:
ALL KIDNEY AND ALL STONE#

PROG:
SS (1) PSTG (167)

SS 2 /C?
USER:
TS :KIDNEY STONE:

PROG:
(65) SCHD (11) QUAL; CONT? (Y/N)

USER:
Y

PROG:
(132) SCHD (22) QUAL; CONT? (Y/N)

USER:
Y

PROG:
SS (2) PSTG (29)

SS 3 /C?
USER:
PRT 3 TI,MH COMPR

(*NLM Search 2, cont.*)
PROG:

1
  TI - Percutaneous nephrolithotripsy. An advancement in kidney stone extraction.
  MH - Case Report ; Human ; Kidney Calculi/*SURGERY ; Male ; Middle Age ; Surgery, Operative/METHODS/TRENDS ; Surgical Nursing

2
  TI - Percutaneous ultrasonic lithotripsy (PUL): kidney stone disintegration.
  MH - Catheterization ; Dilatation ; Human ; Kidney Calculi/*THERAPY ; Ultrasonic Therapy/INSTRUMENTATION/*METHODS ; Ureteral Calculi/*THERAPY ; Urography

3
  TI - Ultrasonic destruction of kidney stones.
  MH - Adult ; Case Report ; Female ; Human ; Kidney Calculi/RADIOGRAPHY/*THERAPY ; Male ; *Ultrasonic Therapy/ADVERSE EFFECTS/INSTRUMENTATION ; Ureteral Calculi/RADIOGRAPHY/THERAPY ; Urography

SS 3 /C?
USER:
KIDNEY CALCULI

PROG:
SS (3) PSTG (685)

SEARCH 3: USING MeSH TERMS WITH SUBHEADINGS AND CHECK TAGS; LIMITING THE RESULTS TO MAJORED MeSH TERMS

Search Topic
The treatment of kidney stones in children or infants. Major aspects only.

Solution
Use the MeSH term KIDNEY CALCULI with the attached subheadings for THERAPY (TH), DRUG THERAPY (DT), RADIOTHERAPY (RT), SURGERY (SU), and DIET THERAPY (DH) to specify the aspects of KIDNEY CALCULI you are interested in. (Other therapy subheadings are also available from *MeSH* and the subheading groups list in Appendix J.) Use the four check tags INFANT; INFANT, NEWBORN; CHILD; and CHILD, PRESCHOOL to specify the age groups desired.

Search Comments
BRS search statement 2—Since MeSH terms are double-posted in BRS, only the words INFANT and CHILD need to be used to retrieve all four check tags.

DIALOG search statement 1—You must attach each subheading separately to MeSH terms (until DIALOG Version 2).

Search statements 7 and 8—Since MeSH terms are double-posted in DIALOG, only the words INFANT and CHILD need to be used to retrieve all four check tags.

Search statement 10—The *COMBINE* command (C) can be used only with search statement numbers and Boolean Operators.

NLM search statements 2–5—In NLM's program, it is easier to "AND" each check tag separately with KIDNEY CALCULI and then "OR" the results. When the *NONE, or no match message is received, that search statement is used again for the next set of terms. If you wanted to save this search and run it in the backfiles—the older file segments of MEDLINE—you would need to include the *NONE search statement by "ORing" it to the statements which had postings, or by using the SAVESEARCH command (which would save your search strategy) before you started this search.

Search statement 6—Although making KIDNEY CALCULI major by typing *KIDNEY CALCULI is a broader approach than re-entering the SUBS APPLY TH, DT, RT, SU, DH command and then typing in *KIDNEY CALCULI, it can result in less precision.

Search 3

BRS:

1-: QS KIDNEY-CALCULI WITH (TH DT RT SU DH)
     KIDNEY-CALCULI-RT   KEYWORD NOT IN DICTIONARY
RESULT   717
2-: INFANT OR CHILD
RESULT   195223
3-: 1 AND 2
RESULT   77
4-: 1.MJ. AND 3
RESULT   44
5-: ..P 4 TI/DOC=10-14

10
TI Surgery of upper tract calculi in children.

11
TI Calyco-ureteroplasty in the management of selected renal calculi.

12
TI [Staghorn calculi in the child. Apropos of 17 cases representing 20
    kidneys].

13
TI Management of infection stones: the Stanford experience.

14
TI Dissolution of cystine calculi by pelviocaliceal irrigation with
    tromethamine-E.

END OF DOCUMENTS

DIALOG:
? SS KIDNEY CALCULI(L)TH OR KIDNEY CALCULI(L)DT OR
     KIDNEY CALCULI(L)RT OR KIDNEY CALCULI(L)SU OR
     KIDNEY CALCULI(L)DH
          1 155 KIDNEY CALCULI(L)TH
          2 114 KIDNEY CALCULI(L)DT
          3   0 KIDNEY CALCULI(L)RT
          4 360 KIDNEY CALCULI(L)SU
          5 15 KIDNEY CALCULI(L)DH
          6 612   1 OR 2 OR 3 OR 4 OR 5

(DIALOG Search 3, cont.)
? SS INFANT OR CHILD
         7 76707 INFANT
         8126613 CHILD
         9163811   7 OR 8
? C9AND6
         10   63 9AND6
? L6/MAJ
         11   405 6/MAJ
? C11AND10
         12   37 11AND10
? T12/6/10-14

12/6/10
1206323   84046323
  Surgery of upper tract calculi in children.

12/6/11
1188782   84028782
  Calyco-ureteroplasty in the management of selected renal calculi.

12/6/12
1137776   83292776
  [Staghorn calculi in the child. Apropos of 17 cases representing 20
    kidneys]
  La lithiase coralliforme de l'enfant. A propos de 17 observations
    representant 20 reins.

12/6/13
0959500   83114500
  Management of infection stones: the Stanford experience.

12/6/14
0957263   83112263
  Dissolution of cystine calculi by pelviocaliceal irrigation with
    tromethamine-E.

NLM:
SS 1 /C?
USER:
SUBS APPLY TH, DT, RT, SU, DH

PROG:
SUBHEADINGS ACCEPTED.

(NLM Search 3, cont.)
SS 1 /C?
USER:
KIDNEY CALCULI
PROG:
SS (1) PSTG (339)

SS 2 /C?
USER:
SUBS CANCEL
PROG:
SUBHEADINGS CANCELLED.

SS 2 /C?
USER:
1 AND INFANT
PROG:
SS (2) PSTG (5)

SS 3 /C?
USER:
1 AND INFANT, NEWBORN
PROG:
*NONE-

SS 3 /C?
USER:
1 AND CHILD, PRESCHOOL
PROG:
SS (3) PSTG (14)

SS 4 /C?
USER:
1 AND CHILD
PROG:
SS (4) PSTG (29)

SS 5 /C?
USER:
2 OR 3 OR 4 OR 1 AND INFANT, NEWBORN
PROG:
SS (5) PSTG (33)

(NLM Search 3, cont.)
SS 6 /C?
USER:
*KIDNEY CALCULI AND 5
PROG:
SS (6) PSTG (24)

SS 7 /C?
USER:
PRT TI 5 SKIP 9
PROG:

10
TI – [New aspects of the therapy of kidney calculi]

11
TI – Surgery of upper tract calculi in children.

12
TI – Calyco-ureteroplasty in the management of selected renal calculi.

13
TI – [Staghorn calculi in the child. Apropos of 17 cases representing 20
     kidneys]

14
TI – Renal tubular acidosis. A new look at treatment of musculoskeletal
     and renal disease.

SEARCH 4: USING EXPLODED MeSH TERMS WITH SUBHEADINGS TO INDICATE RELATIONSHIPS AMONG CONCEPTS

Search Topic

Anesthesia-associated hepatotoxicity. English language articles only. Humans only.

Solution

MeSH term/subheading combinations are needed to indicate the relationship between the anesthetics and the liver diseases. Explosions are used to retrieve the following MeSH terms and their indented, more specific terms—LIVER DISEASES, LIVER, ANESTHESIA, ANESTHETICS, and ANESTHETICS, LOCAL.

Hint

For the adverse effects of a substance, routinely use the subheadings for ADVERSE EFFECTS (AE), TOXICITY (TO), and POISONING (PO). The ways in which these substances cause liver diseases can be expressed with the subheading CHEMICALLY INDUCED (CI) (which is a more specific subheading) and with the subheading ETIOLOGY (ET). How the substances affect the liver can be expressed with the subheading DRUG EFFECTS (DE). Always consider the disease as well as the organ in this type of search topic. In addition, be alert for relevant MeSH terms such as ANESTHESIA and ANESTHETICS that have no cross references.

Search Comments

DIALOG input following set 16—When using the SS command, an individual set number must be expressed by the number with an S in front of it, e.g., S16.

Search 4

BRS:
BRS - SEARCH MODE - ENTER QUERY
```
  1-:  (EX E3.155$ OR EX D14.166$ OR EX D14.211$) WITH (AE TO
       PO)
  RESULT   4639
  2-:  EX C6.552$ WITH (CI ET)
  RESULT   6693
  3-:  EX A3.620$ WITH DE
  RESULT   7169
  4-:  1 AND (2 OR 3)
  RESULT   328
  5-:  ..L/4 LG=EN
  RESULT   262
```
BRS - SEARCH MODE - ENTER QUERY

(BRS Search 4, cont.)
6-:   5 AND HUMAN
RESULT   138
7-:   ..P 6 TI/DOC=1-5.

1
TI Liver damage after halothane anaesthesia: analysis of cases in
    Finnish hospitals in 1972–1981.

2
TI Metabolic disposition and toxicity of cocaine.

3
TI Halothane-associated granulomatous hepatitis.

4
TI Cocaine-mediated hepatotoxicity. A critical review.

5
TI Clinical significance of eosinophilia in the diagnosis of
    halothane-induced liver injury.

END OF DOCUMENTS

DIALOG:
? SS DC=E3.155?(L)AE OR DC=E3.155?(L)TO OR DC=E3.155?(L)PO
          1   1696 DC=E3.155?(L)AE
          2   0 DC=E3.155?(L)TO
          3   0 DC=E3.155?(L)PO
          4   1696   1 OR 2 OR 3
? SS DC=D14.166?(L)AE OR DC=D14.166?(L)TO OR
DC=D14.166?(L)PO
          5   1314 DC=D14.166?(L)AE
          6   372 DC=D14.166?(L)TO
          7   259 DC=D14.166?(L)PO
          8   1938   5 OR 6 OR 7
? SS DC=D14.211?(L)AE OR DC=D14.211?(L)TO OR
DC=D14.211?(L)PO
          9   519 DC=D14.211?(L)AE
         10   104 DC=D14.211?(L)TO
         11   59 DC=D14.211?(L)PO
         12   673   9 OR 10 OR 11
? C4OR8OR12
         13   3862 4OR8OR12
? SS DC=C6.552?(L)CI OR DC=C6.552?(L)ET
         14   1920 DC=C6.552?(L)CI
         15   3828 DC=C6.552?(L)ET
         16   5622 14 OR 15

(DIALOG Search 4, cont.)
? SS DC=A3.620?(L)DE OR S16
　　　　　17　5984　DC=A3.620?(L)DE
　　　　　18　11243　17 OR 16
? C18 AND 13
　　　　　19　　275　18 AND 13
? L19/HUMAN
　　　　　20　　160　19/HUMAN
? SS S20 NOT LA=NONENGLISH
　　　　　21　354880　LA=NONENGLISH
　　　　　22　　112　20 NOT 21
? T22/6/1-5

22/6/1
1389845　84229845
　　Liver damage after halothane anaesthesia: analysis of cases in
　　Finnish hospitals in 1972–1981.

22/6/2
1327156　84167156
　　Metabolic disposition and toxicity of cocaine.

22/6/3
1319256　84159256
　　Halothane-associated granulomatous hepatitis.

22/6/4
1313969　84153969
　　Cocaine-mediated hepatotoxicity. A critical review.

22/6/5
1310008　84150008
　　Clinical significance of eosinophilia in the diagnosis of
　　halothane-induced liver injury.

NLM:
SS 1 /C?
USER:
SUBS APPLY AE, TO, PO

PROG:
SUBHEADINGS ACCEPTED.

(NLM Search 4, cont.)
SS 1 /C?
USER:
EXP ANESTHESIA OR EXP ANESTHETICS OR EXP ANESTHETICS,
LOCAL

PROG:
SS (1) PSTG (1874)

SS 2 /C?
USER:
SUBS CANCEL

PROG:
SUBHEADINGS CANCELLED.

SS 2 /C?
USER:
SUBS APPLY CI, ET

PROG:
SUBHEADINGS ACCEPTED.

SS 2 /C?
USER:
EXP LIVER DISEASES

PROG:
SS (2) PSTG (2864)

SS 3 /C?
USER:
SUBS CANCEL

PROG:
SUBHEADINGS CANCELLED.

SS 3 /C?
USER:
EXP LIVER/DE OR 2

PROG:
SS (3) PSTG (5552)

(NLM Search 4, cont.)
SS 4 /C?
USER:
3 AND 1

PROG:
SS (4) PSTG (126)

SS 5 /C?
USER:
TS (LA) ENG AND HUMAN(MH)

PROG:
(88) SCHD (29) QUAL; CONT? (Y/N)

USER:
Y

PROG:
SS (5) PSTG (44)

SS 6 /C?
USER:
PRT 5 TI

PROG:

1
TI - Liver damage after halothane anaesthesia: analysis of cases in
    Finnish hospitals in 1972–1981.

2
TI - Metabolic disposition and toxicity of cocaine.

3
TI - Halothane-associated granulomatous hepatitis.

4
TI - Cocaine-mediated hepatotoxicity. A critical review.

5
TI - Clinical significance of eosinophilia in the diagnosis of
    halothane-induced liver injury.

SEARCH 5: INCREASING THE PRECISION RATIO IN AN AGE-RELATED TOPIC

Search Topic

Hypertension and the elderly.

Solution

This search topic is deceiving—it seems simply a matter of "ANDing" EXPLODEd HYPERTENSION with the check tag AGED. However, check tags are applied routinely, whether or not they are the main emphasis of an article. When you are dealing with an usual aspect of an age group—such as day care for the aged—you will not be dealing with a very large number of references. However, as you will see from the following searches, in this case there are too many articles indexed to both terms; and when both are majored, there are too few.

There are several ways to deal with this search situation by making EXPLODEd HYPERTENSION major and "ANDing" it to: 1) AGED majored, 2) other majored related MeSH terms, 3) aged-related textwords from titles only, and 4) aged-related journals. Each of the latter three options would also have to be "ANDed" to the check tag AGED, to eliminate irrelevant references.

Hint

There are more textwords and journal titles that could be used in constructing this strategy. If you run several "aged" searches a year, it would be very practical to store a list of geriatrics journal titles and textwords online.[1] (In place of journal title abbreviations, ISSN numbers or journal title codes can be used.)

Search Comments

BRS search statement 2—A single-word majored MeSH term is specified by the SJ qualifier; a single-word minor MeSH term is specified by the SN qualifier. It is necessary to limit to the single-word MeSH term AGED so that you do not retrieve HOMES FOR THE AGED, etc.

DIALOG search statement 2—The letters DF specify a single-word MeSH term qualifier. It is necessary to limit to the single-word MeSH term AGED so that you do not retrieve HOMES FOR THE AGED, etc.

NLM search statement 7—Journal title abbreviation is specified by (TA).

Search 5

BRS:

```
1-:   EX C14.907.489$
RESULT   23849
2-:   1 AND AGED.SJ,SN.
RESULT   4816
```

(BRS Search 5, cont.)
3-:   1.MJ. AND 2
RESULT   3286
4-:   1.MJ. AND AGED.SJ.
RESULT   14
5-:   (ELDER$ OR AGED OR AGING OR AGEING OR SENIOR OR
      GERIATRIC$ OR OLD OR OLDER OR GERONT$).TI,MJ.
RESULT   23959
6-:   (GERIATRICS OR GERONTOLOGIST OR GERONTOLOGY OR
      INT-J-AGING$ OR J-AM-GERI$).SO.
RESULT   2380
7-:   5 OR 6
RESULT   24571
8-:   7 AND 3
RESULT   273
9-:   ..L/8 LG=EN
RESULT   169
BRS – SEARCH MODE – ENTER QUERY
10-:   ..P 9 BIBL,DE/DOC=1-5

1
AU Hamdy-R-C. Davies-A. Arnold-K. Tovey-J-D. Saimbi-S-S. Short-M-D.
   Exton-Smith-A-N.
 TI The short-term effects of reducing elevated blood pressure in elderly
   patients with propranolol and dyazide.
SO Age-Ageing. 1984 Mar. 13(2). P 83–8.
DE ANTIHYPERTENSIVE-AGENTS: tu. BLOOD-PRESSURE: de.
   HYDROCHLOROTHIAZIDE: tu. HYPERTENSION: dt.
   PROPRANOLOL: tu. TRIAMTERENE: tu. AGED.
   CARDIAC-OUTPUT: de. CEREBROVASCULAR-CIRCULATION:
   de. COGNITION: de. COMPARATIVE-STUDY.
   DRUG-COMBINATIONS: tu. ELECTROCARDIOGRAPHY.
   FEMALE. GLOMERULAR-FILTRATION-RATE: de. HUMAN.
   MALE. SUPPORT-NON-U-S-GOVT.

2
AU Applegate-W-B. Mann-J.
 TI Hypertension in the elderly.
SO J-Tenn-Med-Assoc. 1984 Apr. 77(4). P 216.
DE AGED. ANTIHYPERTENSIVE-AGENTS: ad. HYPERTENSION: dt.
   HUMAN.

(BRS Search 5, cont.)

3

AU Drinka-P-J. Nolten-W-E.

TI Hazards of treating osteoporosis and hypertension with calcium, vitamin D, and distal diuretics.

SO J-AM-GER-SOC. 1984 MAY. 32(5). P 83-8.

DE CALCIUM-CARBONATE: ae. DIURETICS-THIAZIDE: ae.
HYPERCALCEMIA: ci. HYPERTENSION: dt. OSTEOPOROSIS: dt.
VITAMIN D: ae.
AGED. CALCIUM: me. CASE-REPORT. DRUG-SYNERGISM.
FEMALE. HUMAN. HYPERTENSION: co. OSTEOPOROSIS: co.

4

AU Hatazawa-J. Yamaguchi-T. Ito-M. Yamaura-H. Matsuzawa-T.

TI Association of hypertension with increased atrophy of brain matter in the elderly.

SO J-Am-Geriatr-Soc. 1984 May. 32(5). P 370-4.

DE BRAIN: pa. HYPERTENSION: co.
ADULT. AGED. AGING. ATROPHY. BRAIN: pp, ra.
COMPARATIVE-STUDY. FEMALE. HUMAN. MALE. MIDDLE-AGE.
TOMOGRAPHY-X-RAY-COMPUTED.

5

AU Currie-W-J. Vandenburg-M-J. Cooper-W-D.

TI Do elderly patients respond differently to treatment with Moducren?

SO Br-J-Clin-Pract. 1984 Mar. 38(3). P 102-6, 119.

DE AMILORIDE: tu. HYDROCHLOROTHIAZIDE: tu. HYPERTENSION:
dt. PYRAZINES: tu. TIMOLOL: tu.
ADULT. AGE-FACTORS. AGED. AMILORIDE: ae.
DRUG-COMBINATIONS: ae, tu. FEMALE. HUMAN.
HYDROCHLOROTHIAZIDE: ae. MALE. MIDDLE-AGE. TIMOLOL:
ae.

END OF DOCUMENTS

DIALOG:

? SS DC=C14.907.489?

       1   20294 DC=C14.907.489?

? SS S1 AND AGED/DF

       2   137714 AGED/DF

       3   4144 1 AND 2

? L1/MAJ

       4   14535 1/MAJ

? C4AND3

       5   2857 4AND3

? L3/MAJ

       6   13 3/MAJ

(DIALOG Search 5, cont.)
? SS ELDER?/TI OR AGED/TI OR AGING/TI OR AGEING/TI OR
SENIOR/TI OR GERIATRIC ?/TI OR OLD/TI OR OLDER/TI OR
GERONT?/TI

7	4057	ELDER?/TI
8	2712	AGED/TI
9	2549	AGING/TI
10	364	AGEING/TI
11	141	SENIOR/TI
12	1287	GERIATRIC?/TI
13	4407	OLD/TI
14	745	OLDER/TI
15	361	GERONT?/TI
16	16054	7 OR 8 OR 9 OR 10 OR 11 OR 12 OR 13 OR 14 OR 15

? SS AGED/DF* OR AGING/DE* OR GERIATRIC?/DE*

17	2232	AGED/DF*
18	6740	AGING/DE*
19	1594	GERIATRIC?/DE*
20	10323	17 OR 18 OR 19

? SS JN=GERIATRIC? OR JN=GERONTOLOGIST OR
JN=GERONTOLOGY OR JN=INT J AGING? OR JN=J AM GER?

21	506	JN=GERIATRIC?
22	451	JN=GERONTOLOGIST
23	246	JN=GERONTOLOGY
24	230	JN=INT J AGING?
25	664	JN=J AM GER?
26	2097	21 OR 22 OR 23 OR 24 OR 25

? C16OR20OR26

27	21006	16 OR 20 OR 26

? C27AND5

28	251	27 AND 5

? SS S28 NOT LA=NONENGLISH

29	354880	LA=NONENGLISH
30	163	28 NOT 29

? T30/2/1-5
30/2/1
1387809   84227809

The short-term effects of reducing elevated blood pressure in elderly
  patients with propranolol and dyazide.
Hamdy RC; Davies A; Arnold K; Tovey JD; Saibi SS; Short MD;
  Exton-Smith AN
Geriatric Medicine, St John's Hospital, London.
Age Ageing (ENGLAND) ,Mar 1984, 13 (2) P 83-8, ISSN 0002-0729
  Journal Code: 2XR

(DIALOG Search 5, cont.)

Languages: ENGLISH

Journal Announcement: 8409

Subfile: INDEX MEDICUS

Tags: Comparative Study; Female; Human; Male; Support, Non-U.S. Gov't

Descriptors: Aged; *Antihypertensive Agents—Therapeutic Use (TU); *Blood Pressure—Drug Effects (DE); Cardiac Output—Drug Effects (DE); Cerebrovascular Circulation—Drug Effects (DE); Cognition—Drug Effects (DE); Drug Combinations—Therapeutic Use (TU); Electrocardiography; ECG; Glomerular Filtration Rate—Drug Effects (DE); *Hydrochlorothiazide—Therapeutic Use (TU); *Hypertension—Drug Therapy (DT); *Propranolol—Therapeutic Use (TU); *Triamterene—Therapeutic Use (TU)

CAS Registry No.: 14124-50-6 .(dyazide); 396-01-0 .(Triamterene); 525-66-6 .(Propranolol); 58-93-5 .(Hydrochlorothiazide)

30/2/2

1377772   84217772

Hypertension in the elderly.

Applegate WB: Mann J

J Tenn Med Assoc (UNITED STATES) ,Apr 1984, 77 (4) P 216, ISSN 0040-3318 Journal Code: K7J

Languages: ENGLISH

Journal Announcement: 8409

Subfile: INDEX MEDICUS

Tags: Human

Descriptors: *Aged; *Antihypertensive Agents—Administration and Dosage (AD); *Hypertension—Drug Therapy (DT)

30/2/3

1346645   84186645

Hazards of treating osteoporosis and hypertension concurrently with calcium, vitamin D, and distal diuretics.

Drinka PJ; Nolten WE

Department of Medicine, University of Wisconsin Medical School, Madison.

J Am Geriatr Soc (UNITED STATES) ,May 1984, 32(5) P 405-7, ISSN 0002-8614 Journal Code: H6V

Languages: ENGLISH

Journal Announcement: 8408

Subfile: INDEX MEDICUS

Tags: Case Report; Female; Human

Descriptors: Aged; *Calcium Carbonate—Adverse Effects (AE); Calcium—Metabolism (ME); *Diuretics, Thiazide—Adverse Effects (AE); Drug Synergism; *Hypercalcemia—Chemically

(*DIALOG Search 5, Cont.*)
Induced (CI); Hypertension—Complications (CO);
*Hypertension—Drug Therapy (DT); Osteoporosis—
Complications (CO); *Osteoporosis—Drug Therapy (DT); *Vitamin
D—Adverse Effects (AE)
CAS Registry No.: 1406-16-2 .(Vitamin D); 471-34-1 .(Calcium
Carbonate); 7440-70-2 .(Calcium).

30/2/4
1346638   84186638
Association of hypertension with increased atrophy of brain matter
in the elderly.
Hatazawa J; Yamaguchi T; Ito M; Yamaura H; Matsuzawa T
Department of Radiology and Nuclear Medicine, Tohoku University,
Miyagi, Japan.
J Am Geriatr Soc (UNITED STATES) ,May 1984, 32 (5) P 370–4, ISSN
0002-8614 Journal Code: H6V
Languages: ENGLISH
Journal Announcement: 8408
Subfile: INDEX MEDICUS
Tags: Comparative Study; Female; Human; Male
Descriptors: Adult; Aged; Aging; Atrophy; *Brain—Pathology (PA);
Brain—Physiopathology (PP); Brain—Radiography (RA);
*Hypertension—Complications (CO); Middle Age; Tomography,
X-Ray Computed; CT XRAY

30/2/5
1338902   84178902
Do elderly patients respond differently to treatment with
Moducren?
Currie WJ; Vandenburg MJ; Cooper WD
Br J Clin Pract (ENGLAND) ,Mar 1984, 38 (3) P 102–6, 119, ISSN
0007-0947 Journal Code: AVK
Languages: ENGLISH
Journal Announcement: 8408
Subfile: INDEX MEDICUS
Tags: Female; Human; Male
Descriptors: Adult; Age Factors; Aged; Amiloride—Adverse Effects
(AE); *Amiloride—Therapeutic Use (TU); Drug Combinations—
Adverse Effects (AE); Drug Combinations—Therapeutic Use (TU);
Hydrochlorothiazide—Adverse Effects (AE); *Hydrochlorothiazide
—Therapeutic Use (TU); *Hypertension—Drug Therapy (DT);
Middle Age; *Pyrazines—Therapeutic Use (TU); Timolol—Adverse
Effects (AE); *Timolol—Therapeutic Use (TU)
CAS Registry No.: 2609-46-3 .(Amiloride); 26839-75-8 .(Timolol);
58-93-5 .(Hydrochlorothiazide); 73788-01-9 .(moducren).

NLM:
SS 1 /C?
USER:
EXP HYPERTENSION AND AGED

PROG:
TIME OVFLW: CONT? (Y/N)

USER:
Y

PROG:
SS (1) PSTG (2075)

SS 2 /C?
USER:
EXP *HYPERTENSION AND AGED

PROG:
TIME OVFLW: CONT? (Y/N)

USER:
Y

PROG:
SS (2) PSTG (1461)

SS 3 /C?
USER:
EXP *HYPERTENSION AND *AGED

PROG:
SS (3) PSTG (9)

SS 4 /C?
USER:
(TW) ALL ELDER: OR AGED OR AGING OR AGEING OR SENIOR OR

PROG:
CNT 4

USER:
ALL GERIATRIC: OR OLD OR OLDER OR ALL GERONT:

(NLM Search 5, cont.)
PROG:
TIME OVFLW: CONT? (Y/N)

USER:
Y

PROG:
TIME OVFLW: CONT? (Y/N)

USER:
Y

PROG:
SS (4) PSTG (29065)

SS 5 /C?
USER:
4 AND 2

PROG:
SS (5) PSTG (213)

SS 6 /C?
USER:
TS :ELDER: OR :AGED: OR :AGING: OR :AGEING: OR :SENIOR: OR

PROG:
CNT 6

USER:
:GERIATRIC: OR :OLD: OR :GERONT:

PROG:
(65) SCHD (38) QUAL; CONT? (Y/N)

USER:
Y

PROG:
(125) SCHD (71) QUAL; CONT? (Y/N)

USER:
Y

(NLM Search 5, cont.)
PROG:
(200) SCHD (125) QUAL; CONT? (Y/N)

USER:
Y

PROG:
SS (6) PSTG (132)

SS 7 /C?
USER:
(TA) GERIATRICS OR GERONTOLOGIST OR GERONTOLOGY OR

PROG:
CNT 7

USER:
INT J AGING: OR J AM GER:

PROG:
SS (7) PSTG (1174)

SS 8 /C?
USER:
*AGING OR ALL *GERIATRIC:

PROG:
SS (8) PSTG (4043)

SS 9 /C?
USER:
7 OR 8

PROG:
SS (9) PSTG (4903)

SS 10 /C?
USER:
9 AND 2 OR 6 OR 3

PROG:
SS (10) PSTG (141)

(*NLM Search 5, cont.*)
SS 11 /C?
USER:
10 AND NOT FOR(LA)

PROG:
TIME OVFLW: CONT? (Y/N)

USER:
Y

PROG:
SS (11) PSTG (95)

SS 12 /C?
USER:
PRT COMPR INCLUDE MH 5

PROG:

1
AU - Hamdy RC ; Davies A ; Arnold K ; Tovey JD ; Saimbi SS ; Short MD ;
      Exton-Smith AN
 TI - The short-term effects of reducing elevated blood pressure in
      elderly patients with propranolol and dyazide.
MH - Aged ; Antihypertensive Agents/*THERAPEUTIC USE ; Blood
      Pressure/*DRUG EFFECTS ; Cardiac Output/*DRUG
      EFFECTS ; Cerebrovascular Circulation/DRUG EFFECTS ;
      Cognition/DRUG EFFECTS ; Comparative Study ; Drug
      Combinations/THERAPEUTIC USE ; Electrocardiography ; Female ;
      Glomerular Filtration Rate/DRUG EFFECTS ; Human ;
      Hydrochlorothiazide/*THERAPEUTIC USE ;
      Hypertension/*DRUG THERAPY ; Male ;
      Propranolol/*THERAPEUTIC USE ; Support, Non-U.S. Gov't ;
      Triamterene/*THERAPEUTIC USE
 SO - Age Ageing 1984 Mar;13(2):83-8.

2
AU - Applegate WB ; Mann J
 TI - Hypertension in the elderly.
MH - *Aged ; Antihypertensive Agents/*ADMINISTRATION &
      DOSAGE ; Human ; Hypertension/*DRUG THERAPY
 SO - J Tenn Med Assoc 1984 Apr;77(4):216.

(NLM Search 5, cont.)

3
 AU - Drinka P ; Nolten WE
  TI - Hazards of treating osteoporosis and hypertension concurrently
       with calcium, vitamin D, and distal diuretics.
 MH - Aged ; Calcium Carbonate/*ADVERSE EFFECTS ; Calcium/
       METABOLISM ; Case Report ; Diuretics, Thiazide/*ADVERSE
       EFFECTS ; Drug Synergism ; Female ; Human ;
       Hypercalcemia/*CHEMICALLY INDUCED ;
       Hypertension/COMPLICATIONS/*DRUG THERAPY ;
       Osteoporosis/COMPLICATIONS/*DRUG THERAPY ; Vitamin
       D/*ADVERSE EFFECTS
 SO - J Am Geriatr Soc 1984 May;32(5):405-7.

4
 AU - Hatazawa J ; Yamaguchi T ; Ito M ; Yamaura H ; Matsuzawa T
  TI - Association of hypertension with increased atrophy of brain matter
       in the elderly.
 MH - Adult ; Aged ; Aging ; Atrophy ; Brain/*PATHOLOGY/
       PHYSIOPATHOLOGY/RADIOGRAPHY ; Comparative Study ;
       Female ; Human ; Hypertension/*COMPLICATIONS ; Male ;
       Middle Age ; Tomography, X-Ray Computed
 SO - J Am Geriatr Soc 1984 May;32(5):370-4.

5
 AU - Currie WJ ; Vandenburg MJ ; Cooper WD
  TI - Do elderly patients respond differently to treatment with
       Moducren?
 MH - Adult ; Age Factors ; Aged ; Amiloride/ADVERSE EFFECTS/
       *THERAPEUTIC USE ; Drug Combinations/ADVERSE
       EFFECTS/THERAPEUTIC USE ; Female ; Human ;
       Hydrochlorothiazide/ADVERSE EFFECTS/*THERAPEUTIC USE ;
       Hypertension/*DRUG THERAPY ; Male ; Middle Age ;
       Pyrazines/*THERAPEUTIC USE ; Timolol/ADVERSE
       EFFECTS/*THERAPEUTIC USE
 SO - Br J Clin Pract 1984 Mar;38(3):102-6, 119.

SEARCH 6: RETROSPECTIVE SEARCHING FOR A CONCEPT NOT PREVIOUSLY EXPRESSED BY A SPECIFIC MeSH TERM

Search Topic
Non-insulin dependent diabetes mellitus.

Solution
DIABETES MELLITUS, NON-INSULIN DEPENDENT became a MeSH term in 1984. Before that, textwords had to be "ANDed" with DIABETES MELLITUS.

Always check the previously-indexed-under section of *MeSH* for earlier indexing of a new term. For the purposes of brevity, only three ways have been selected to express this search topic in textwords: "non-insulin-dependent," "adult onset," and "type II." It is important to express the concept of "II" in Roman numerals (II), words (two), and numbers (2) to increase retrieval.

Hint
Numbers must be enclosed with single quotation marks in BRS so that they won't be confused with search statement numbers. Numbers are not directly searchable through NLM—the stringsearch command must be used. Check monographs and other materials for possible textwords to use in this search.

Search Comments
NLM search statement 4—CNT 4 is a continuation cue message meaning that you can continue your previous line of search terms ending with an "OR." The (#) SCHD (#) QUAL; CONT? (Y/N) message occurs during a stringsearch operation when the program stops after processing a group of citations and asks whether you want to continue this process.

BRS:
1-: DIABETES-MELLITUS-NON-INSULIN-DEPENDENT
RESULT   318
2-: TYPE ADJ ('2' OR II OR TWO)
RESULT   5550
3-: ADULT ADJ ONSET OR NON ADJ INSULIN ADJ DEPENDENT
RESULT   900
4-: 2 OR 3
RESULT   6297
5-: 4 AND DIABETES-MELLITUS OR 1
RESULT   795
6-: DIABETES-MELLITUS$.MJ. AND 5
RESULT   703
7-: ..P 6 TI/DOC=1-5

(BRS Search 6, cont.)

1

TI Diabetes alert study: weight history and upper body obesity in diabetic and non-diabetic Mexican American adults.

2

TI Abnormal zinc metabolism in type II diabetes mellitus [letter].

3

TI Hepatic glucose-6-phosphatase activity in non-insulin dependent diabetics. Effect of enzyme-inducing drugs.

4

TI Effect of dietary fibre on blood glucose, plasma immunoreactive insulin, C-peptide and GIP responses in non insulin dependent (type 2) diabetics and controls.

5

TI The combination of insulin and sulphonylurea in the treatment of secondary drug failure in patients with type II diabetes.

END OF DOCUMENTS

DIALOG:
? SS DIABETES MELLITUS, NON-INSULIN-DEPENDENT
       1   318 DIABETES MELLITUS,
                NON-INSULIN-DEPENDENT
? SS TYPE(W)2 OR TYPE(W)II OR TYPE(W)TWO
       2   1725 TYPE(W)2
       3   3126 TYPE(W)II
       4   20 TYPE(W)TWO
       5   4864 2 OR 3 OR 4
? SS ADULT(W)ONSET OR NON(W)INSULIN(W)DEPENDENT
       6   236 ADULT(W)ONSET
       7   627 NON(W)INSULIN(W)DEPENDENT
       8   851 6 OR 7
? SS (S5 OR S8) AND DIABETES MELLITUS
       9   8821 DIABETES MELLITUS
     10   482 (5 OR 8) AND 9
? C1OR10
     11   770 1OR10
? SS DIABETES MELLITUS?/DE*
     12   9967 DIABETES MELLITUS?/DE*
? C11 AND 12
     13   680 11AND12
? T13/8/1-5

(DIALOG Search 6, cont.)
13/8/1
1389887   84229887
   Diabetes alert study: weight history and upper body obesity in
   diabetic and non-diabetic Mexican American adults.

13/8/2
1388523   84228523
   Abnormal zinc metabolism in type II diabetes mellitus [letter]

13/8/3
1387478   84227478
   Hepatic glucose-6-phosphatase activity in non-insulin dependent :
   diabetics. Effect of enzyme-inducing drugs.

13/8/4
1387459   84227459
   Effect of dietary fibre on blood glucose, plasma immunoreactive
   insulin, C-peptide and GIP responses in non insulin dependent
   (type 2) diabetics and controls.

13/8/5
1386943   84226943
   The combination of insulin and sulphonylurea in the treatment of
   secondary drug failure in patients with type II diabetes.

NLM:
SS 1 /C?
USER:
DIABETES MELLITUS, NON-INSULIN-DEPENDENT
PROG:
SS (1) PSTG (318)

SS 2 /C?
USER:
DIABETES MELLITUS
PROG:
SS (2) PSTG (4052)

SS 3 /C?
USER:
2 AND TYPE(TW)
PROG:
SS (3) PSTG (392)

SS 4 /C?
USER:

(NLM Search 6, cont.)
TS :TYPE#2: OR :TYPE#2:(AB) OR :TYPE#II: OR :TYPE#II:(AB) OR
PROG:
CNT 4

USER:
:TYPE#TWO: OR :TYPE#TWO:(AB)
PROG:
(97) SCHD (39) QUAL; CONT? (Y/N)

USER:
Y
PROG:
(197) SCHD (79) QUAL; CONT? (Y/N)

USER:
Y
PROG:
(304) SCHD (122) QUAL; CONT? (Y/N)

USER:
y
PROG:
SS (4) PSTG (155)

SS 5 /C?
USER:
2 AND ADULT(TW) AND ONSET (TW)
PROG:
SS (5) PSTG (25)

SS 6 /C?
USER:
2 AND NON(TW) AND INSULIN(TW) AND DEPENDENT(TW)
PROG:
SS (6) PSTG (207)

SS 7 /C?
USER:
5 OR 6
PROG:
SS (7) PSTG (232)

(*NLM Search 6, cont.*)
SS 8 /C?
USER:
TS :ADULT#ONSET: OR :ADULT#ONSET:(AB) OR
:NON#INSULIN#DEPENDENT: OR
PROG:
CNT 8

USER:
:NON#INSULIN#DEPENDENT:(AB)
PROG:
(89) SCHD (71) QUAL; CONT? (Y/N)

USER:
Y
PROG:
(181) SCHD (143) QUAL; CONT? (Y/N)

USER:
Y
PROG:
SS (8) PSTG (190)

SS 9 /C?
USER:
1 OR 4 OR 8
PROG:
SS (9) PSTG (602)

SS 10 /C?
USER:
ALL *DIABETES MELLITUS: AND 9
PROG:
SS (10) PSTG (525)

SS 11 /C?
USER:
PRT 5 TI
PROG:

1
TI - Diabetes alert study: weight history and upper body obesity in
    diabetic and non-diabetic Mexican American adults.

2
TI - Abnormal zinc metabolism in type II diabetes mellitus [letter]

(NLM Search 6, cont.)

3

TI - Hepatic glucose-6-phosphatase activity in non-insulin dependent diabetics. Effect of enzyme-inducing drugs.

4

TI - Effect of dietary fibre on blood glucose, plasma immunoreactive insulin, C-peptide and GIP responses in non insulin dependent (type 2) diabetics and controls.

5

TI - The combination of insulin and sulphonylurea in the treatment of secondary drug failure in patients with type II diabetes.

Reference

[1]Green EW. Searching the MEDLARS file for information about the elderly. Bull Med Libr Assoc 1981;69:359–67.

Appendices

Appendix A: Directory of MEDLINE Vendors and Selected Database Access Software

MEDLINE VENDORS
Bibliographic Retrieval Services, Inc. (BRS)
  1200 Route 7
  Latham, New York, 12110
  (800) 345-4277
  (800) 553-5566 (New York State)
  User-friendly systems: BRS/AFTER DARK, BRS/SAUNDERS COLLEAGUE

DIALOG Information Services, Inc.
  3460 Hillview Avenue
  Palo Alto, California 94304
  (800) 227-1960
  (800) 982-5838 (California)
  User-friendly system: KNOWLEDGE INDEX

National Library of Medicine
  8600 Rockville Pike
  Bethesda, Maryland, 20209
  (800) 638-8480
  (301) 496-6193 (Maryland)

Beth Israel Hospital
PAPERCHASE
  330 Brookline Avenue
  Boston, Massachusetts 02215
  (617) 735-2253

DATABASE ACCESS SOFTWARE PACKAGES
Menlo Corporation
IN-SEARCH
  4633 Old Ironsides Drive Suite 400
  Santa Clara, California 95050
  (408) 986-1200

SDC Information Services
ORBIT SEARCHMASTER
  2500 Colorado Ave.
  Santa Monica, California, 90406
  (800) 421-7229
  (800) 352-6689 (California)

Institute for Scientific Information
SCI-MATE UNIVERSAL ONLINE SEARCHER
  3501 Market Street
  University City Science Center
  Philadelphia, Pennsylvania 19104
  (800) 523-4092

Appendix B: MEDLINE File Divisions

BRS		**DIALOG**		**NLM**	
MeSH	1979+	FILE 154	1980+	MEDLINE	1983+
MS78	1975–78	FILE 153	1973–79	B80	1980–82
MS74	1971–74	FILE 152	1966–72	B77	1977–79
MS70	1966–70			B75	1975–76
				B71	1971–74
				B66	1966–70

PRINTHOLD:
Available only at BRS
for any division or
combination of divi-
sions except for
MeSH.

OPTIONS INCLUDE:
all
6678
6674
7178, etc.

All file divisions can be searched simultaneously and results printed offline.	Each file division must be searched individually, one at a time.	All file divisions can be searched simultaneously and results printed off-line.
Results can be "merged" in one sorted list.	Online sort feature. Each file division is sorted separately.	Each file division is sorted separately.

Appendix C: Online Vendor Searching Aids —
General and MEDLINE-Related

BRS:

BRS AidPage for MEDLARS-On-Line (MEDLINE). Latham, N.Y.: BRS, 1984.
BRS Brief System Guide.
BRS Bulletin. Vol. 1, 1977–
BRS MeSH Training Syllabus.
BRS System Reference Manual. Scotia, N.Y.: BRS, 1981.
MeSH Database Guide. (database chapter)

DIALOG:

Chronolog. Vol. 1, 1973–
DIALOG Seminar for Medical Professionals. (training workbook)
Guide to DIALOG Searching. Palo Alto: Lockheed DIALOG, 1979.
MEDLINE. (blue sheet)
MEDLINE. DIALOG Information Retrieval Service. (database chapter)
MEDLINE Seminar. (training workbook)
Pocket Guide to DIALOG Information Retrieval Service. (updated regularly)

NLM:

The Basics of Searching MEDLINE: A Guide for the Health Professional. 1984.
Course Workbook. Initial Online Training Class NLM. (includes MEDLINE section)
National Library of Medicine Online Services Reference Manual, 1982 and *Supplement, 1984.* Springfield, VA: NTIS, 1984. (PB84-186816)
NLM Technical Bulletin, No. 1, 1970–

Appendix D: Stopwords

BRS STOPWORDS
(total = 72)

a	if	than
about	in	that
all	into	the
among	is	their
an	it	these
and	its	they
are	made	this
as	make	those
at	many	through
be	may	to
been	more	toward
between	most	upon
both	must	used
buy	no	using
by	not	was
do	of	were
during	on	what
each	or	which
either	same	while
for	several	who
found	some	will
from	such	with
further		within
has		would
have		
however		

From: *BRS System Reference Manual,* 1982

DIALOG
(total = 9)

an	for	the
and	from	to
by	of	with

From: *Guide to DIALOG Searching,* 1979

NLM
(total = 253)

a	affected	against	although	another
abs	affecting	all	always	any
about	affects	almost	among	anyone
accordingly	after	already	an	apparently
affect	again	also	and	are

(NLM Stopwords cont.)

arise	found	mostly	rather	them
as	from	much	readily	then
aside	further	mug	really	there
at	gave	must	recently	therefore
away	gets	nearly	refs	these
be	give	necessarily	regarding	they
became	given	neither	regardless	this
because	giving	next	relatively	those
become	gone	no	respectively	though
becomes	got	none	resulted	through
been	had	nor	resulting	throughout
before	hardly	normally	results	to
being	has	nos	said	too
between	have	not	same	toward
biol	having	noted	seem	under
both	here	now	seen	unless
briefly	how	obtain	several	until
but	however	obtained	shall	up
by	if	of	should	upon
came	immediately	often	show	use
can	importance	on	showed	used
cannot	important	only	shown	usefully
certain	in	or	shows	usefulness
certainly	into	other	significantly	using
chem	is	ought	similar	usually
copyright	it	our	similarly	various
could	its	out	since	very
did	itself	overall	slightly	was
different	just	owing	so	were
do	keep	particularly	some	what
does	kept	past	sometime	when
done	kg	perhaps	somewhat	where
due	km	please	soon	whether
during	knowledge	poorly	specifically	which
each	largely	possible	state	while
effect	like	possibly	states	who
effects	made	potentially	strongly	whose
either	mainly	predominantly	substantially	why
else	make	present	successfully	widely
enough	many	previously	such	will
especially	may	primarily	sufficiently	within
etc	mg	probably	than	without
ever	might	prompt	that	would
every	ml	promptly	the	yet
following	more	quickly	their	
for	most	quite	theirs	

Also: numbers composed of all numerics are stopwords.

FROM: *NLM Online Services Reference Manual*, 1982.

Appendix E: MEDLINE Search Aids Produced by the National Library of Medicine

The following reference tools are produced by the National Library of Medicine and published by the National Technical Information Service (NTIS), 5285 Port Royal Road, Springfield, Va., 22161.

Medical Subject Headings, Annotated Alphabetical List. (Annual)
Medical Subject Headings, Tree Structures. (Annual)
Permuted MeSH. (Annual)

In addition to the three-volume *MeSH*, some other NLM publications are useful for the MEDLINE searcher. They are listed below in alphabetical order.

Cumulated List of New Medical Subject Headings, 1963–73 provides previously indexed information for MeSH terms. It is no longer updated.

List of Journals Indexed in Index Medicus is an annual publication which lists *Index Medicus* journals alphabetically by abbreviation, full title, broad subject field, ISSN, and country of origin. The subject listing can be used to include specific journals in a search strategy. The letter "s" before a title indicates that this journal has been only selectively indexed. Such journals include *Science* and *Scientific American*.

List of Serials for Online Users is an annual publication listing MEDLINE, HEALTH, and POPLINE journals by abbreviation, full title, ISSN, and journal title code.

Medical Subject Headings—Supplementary Chemical Records, 1985, contains records of more than 23,000 chemicals which have been mentioned in a significant way since 1970 in journals indexed in MEDLINE. These chemicals do not have specific MeSH terms in the printed *MeSH*. *Medical Subject Headings—Supplementary Chemical Records,* also known as the *Chemical Tool*, supplements the Category D section of the *Tree Structures* by providing the generic name of the compound, synonyms identified in indexed MEDLINE journals, CAS registry numbers or the EC number, the MeSH term under which the compound will appear in *Index Medicus*, and additional indexing information.

✓ *MEDLARS Indexing Manual, Part II, 1984* is the source of all indexing rules for MEDLARS. This manual is an excellent, detailed, instructive guide. Part I, published separately, describes the bibliographic principles of MEDLARS indexing, and is of less use to the MEDLINE searcher than Part II, which is essential to the understanding of NLM's indexing policies.

Technical Notes—MEDLARS Indexing Instructions, 1984 provides more specific information about indexing, but not as systematically as the *Indexing Manual*.

Technical Notes—MEDLARS Indexing Instructions: Tumor Key Supplement, 1984 is a guide to the use of correct MeSH terms for various histologic types of neoplasms. It provides the cross references that are omitted from *MeSH*. Sometimes, the earlier editions of this publication will mention the histologic type of neoplasm you are looking for. Don't discard these editions.

Appendix F: Cascades/Pre-explodes, 1985

DIALOG Cascades

Descriptor Category	Descriptor Code Tree Number
ABNORMALITIES	DC=C16.131.
ACIDS, ACYCLIC	DC=D2.241.81.
ACIDS, CARBOCYCLIC	DC=D2.241.223.
ALCOHOLS	DC=D2.33.
ALKALOIDS	DC=D3.132.
AMERICA	DC=Z1.107.
AMIDES	DC=D2.65.
AMINES	DC=D2.92.
AMINO ACIDS	DC=D12.125.
ANALGESICS	DC=D14.73.
ANTI-INFLAMMATORY AGENTS	DC=D26.74.
ANTIBIOTICS	DC=D20.85.
ANTIBODIES	DC=D24.611.125.
ANTIHYPERTENSIVE AGENTS	DC=D18.162.
ANTILIPEMIC AGENTS	DC=D10.162.
ANTINEOPLASTIC AGENTS	DC=D22.204.
BACTERIA	DC=B3.
BACTERIAL INFECTIONS	DC=C1.252.
BEHAVIOR	DC=F1.145.
BEHAVIOR AND BEHAVIOR MECHANISMS	DC=F1.
BEHAVIORAL AND MENTAL DISORDERS	DC=F3.
BEHAVIORAL SYMPTOMS	DC=F3.126.
BINDING SITES	DC=G6.184.154.
BIOCHEMICAL PHENOMENA	DC=G6.184.
BIOCHEMICAL PHENOMENA, METABOLISM, NUTRITION	DC=G6.
BIOLOGICAL FACTORS	DC=D24.185.
BLOOD	DC=A15.145.
BLOOD PROTEINS	DC=D12.776.124.
BRAIN	DC=A8.186.211.
BRAIN DISEASES	DC=C10.228.140.
CARBOHYDRATES	DC=D9.203.
CARBOXYLIC ACIDS	DC=D2.241.
CARDIOTONIC AGENTS	DC=D18.222.
CARDIOVASCULAR AGENTS	DC=D18.
CARDIOVASCULAR DISEASES	DC=C14.
CARDIOVASCULAR SYSTEM	DC=A7.
CARDIOVASCULAR SYSTEM PHYSIOLOGY	DC=G9.330.
CELL PHYSIOLOGY	DC=G4.335.
CELLS	DC=A11.
CENTRAL NERVOUS SYSTEM	DC=A8.186.

Source: *Chronolog* 1985

Descriptor Category	Descriptor Code Tree Number
CENTRAL NERVOUS SYSTEM DISEASES	DC=C10.228.
CHEMISTRY	DC=H1.181.
CHEMISTRY, ANALYTICAL	DC=E5.196.
CHEMISTRY, PHYSICAL	DC=H1.181.529.
CIRCULATORY, RESPIRATORY PHYSIOLOGY	DC=G9.
DENTISTRY	DC=E6.
DIAGNOSIS, LABORATORY	DC=E1.223.
DIGESTIVE SYSTEM DISEASES	DC=C6.
ELEMENTS	DC=D1.268.
ENVIRONMENT	DC=G3.230.
ENZYME INHIBITORS	DC=D8.373.
ENZYMES	DC=D8.586.
EQUIPMENT AND SUPPLIES	DC=E7.
EUROPE	DC=Z1.542.
EYE DISEASES	DC=C11.
FATTY ACIDS	DC=D10.516.251.
FUNGI	DC=B5.354.
GASTROINTESTINAL DISEASES	DC=C6.405.
GENETICS	DC=G5.
GENITAL DISEASES, FEMALE	DC=C13.371.
GLOBULINS	DC=D12.776.377.
GLYCOSIDES	DC=D9.203.408.
HEALTH FACILITIES	DC=N2.278.
HEALTH SERVICES	DC=N2.421.
HEART DISEASES	DC=C14.280.
HEMATOLOGIC AGENTS	DC=D19.461.
HEMATOLOGIC DISEASES	DC=C15.378.
HETEROCYCLIC CPDS, 1-RING	DC=D3.383.
HETEROCYCLIC CPDS, 2-RING	DC=D3.438.
HETEROCYCLIC CPDS, 3-RING	DC=D3.494.
HORMONES	DC=D6.472.
HORMONES, SYNTHETIC	DC=D6.597.
HYDROCARBONS	DC=D2.455.
HYDROCARBONS, CYCLIC	DC=D2.455.426.
HYDROLASES	DC=D8.586.277.
IMMUNITY	DC=G4.610.
IMMUNOLOGIC FACTORS	DC=D24.611.
IMMUNOLOGIC TECHNICS	DC=E5.478.
INFECTION	DC=C1.539.
INTESTINAL DISEASES	DC=C6.405.469.
LIPIDS	DC=D10.516.
LIVER DISEASES	DC=C6.552.
LUNG DISEASES	DC=C8.381.
MAMMALS	DC=B2.649.
MENTAL DISORDERS	DC=F3.709.
MENTAL PROCESSES	DC=F2.463.
METABOLIC DISEASES	DC=C18.452.

Descriptor Category	Descriptor Code Tree Number
METABOLISM	DC=G6.535.
METALS	DC=D1.552.
MISCELLANEOUS TECHNICS	DC=E5.
MOUTH AND TOOTH DISEASES	DC=C7.
MUSCULOSKELETAL DISEASES	DC=C5.
NAMED GROUPS BY OCCUPATION	DC=M1.526.
NEOPLASMS	DC=C4.
NEOPLASMS BY HISTOLOGIC TYPE	DC=C4.557.
NEOPLASMS BY SITE	DC=C4.588.
NERVOUS SYSTEM	DC=A8.
NERVOUS SYSTEM DISEASES	DC=C10.
NERVOUS SYSTEM PHYSIOLOGY	DC=G11.561.
NEUROLOGIC MANIFESTATIONS	DC=C10.597.
NORTH AMERICA	DC=Z1.107.567.
NUCLEIC ACIDS	DC=D13.444.
NUCLEOSIDES	DC=D13.570.
NUCLEOTIDES	DC=D13.695.
ORGANIZATION AND ADMINISTRATION	DC=N4.452.
OXIDOREDUCTASES	DC=D8.586.682.
PESTICIDES	DC=D5.723.
PHYSICS	DC=H1.671.
PHYSIOLOGY, GENERAL	DC=G7.
PREGNANCY	DC=G8.520.769.
PREGNANCY COMPLICATIONS	DC=C13.703.
PROTEINS	DC=D12.776.
PSYCHOLOGIC PROCESSES AND PRINCIPLES	DC=F2.
PSYCHOLOGY, SOCIAL	DC=F1.829.
PSYCHOTROPIC DRUGS	DC=D15.236.
PUBLIC HEALTH	DC=G3.850.
REPRODUCTION	DC=G8.520.
REPRODUCTION, UROGENITAL PHYSIOLOGY	DC=G8.
RESPIRATORY TRACT DISEASES	DC=C8.
RIBONUCLEOTIDES	DC=D13.695.827.
RNA VIRUSES	DC=B4.909.777.
RODENTIA	DC=B2.649.865.
SIGNS AND SYMPTOMS	DC=C23.888.
SKIN DISEASES	DC=C17.
SOCIOLOGY	DC=I1.880.
STEROIDS	DC=D4.808.
SULFUR COMPOUNDS	DC=D2.886.
SURGERY, OPERATIVE	DC=E4.
SURGICAL EQUIPMENT	DC=E7.858.
TECHNOLOGY, MEDICAL	DC=E5.909
TRANSFERASES	DC=D8.586.913.
UNITED STATES	DC=Z1.107.567.875.
UROLOGIC DISEASES	DC=C12.777.
VASCULAR DISEASES	DC=C14.907.

Descriptor Category	Descriptor Code Tree Number
VERTEBRATE VIRUSES	DC=B4.909.
VERTEBRATES	DC=B2.
VIRUS DISEASES	DC=C2.
VIRUSES	DC=B4.
VITAMINS	DC=D11.786.
WOUNDS AND INJURIES	DC=C21.866.

NLM Pre-explodes, 1985

Pre-explosion Name (PX)	Tree No.
ABNORMALITIES	C16.131
ANTIBIOTICS	D20.85
ANTIBODIES	D24.611.125
BACTERIA	B3
BACTERIAL INFECTIONS	C1.252
BEHAVIOR	F1.145
BEHAVIOR AND BEHAVIOR MECHANISMS	F1
BEHAVIORAL AND MENTAL DISORDERS	F3
BIOCHEM PHENOM METAB	G6
BLOOD PROTEINS	D12.776.124
BRAIN	A8.186.211
CARBOHYDRATES	D9.203
CARDIOVASCULAR AGENTS	D18
CARDIOVASCULAR DISEASES	C14
CARDIOVASCULAR SYSTEM	A7
CELLS	A11
CENTRAL NERVOUS SYSTEM	A8.186
CENTRAL NERVOUS SYSTEM DISEASES	C10.228
CHEMISTRY, ANALYTICAL	E5.196
CIRCULATORY, RESPIRATORY PHYSIOLOGY	G9
DENTISTRY	E6
DIAGNOSIS, LABORATORY	E1.223
DIGESTIVE SYSTEM DISEASES	C6
ENZYMES	D8.586
EQUIPMENT AND SUPPLIES	E7
GASTROINTESTINAL DISEASES	C6.405
GENETICS	G5
HEALTH FACILITIES	N2.278
HEALTH SERVICES	N2.421
HEART DISEASES	C14.280
HORMONES	D6.472
IMMUNITY	G4.610
IMMUNOLOGIC FACTORS	D24.611
LIPIDS	D10.516
MAMMALS	B2.649
MENTAL DISORDERS	F3.709

Source: *Alphabetic Annotated List*, 1985.

Descriptor Category	Descriptor Code Tree Number
METABOLIC DISEASES	C18.452
METALS	D1.552
MISCELLANEOUS TECHNICS	E5
MOUTH AND TOOTH DISEASES	C7
MUSCULOSKELETAL DISEASES	C5
NEOPLASMS	C4
NERVOUS SYSTEM	A8
NERVOUS SYSTEM DISEASES	C10
NEUROLOGIC MANIFESTATIONS	C10.597
ORGANIZATION AND ADMINISTRATION	N4.452
PHYSIOLOGY, GENERAL	G7
PROTEINS	D12.776
PSYCHOLOGIC PROCESSES PRINCIPLES	F2
REPRODUCTION, UROGENITAL PHYSIOLOGY	G8
RESPIRATORY TRACT DISEASES	C8
RODENTIA	B2.649.865
SIGNS AND SYMPTOMS	C23.888
SKIN DISEASES	C17
STEROIDS	D4.808
SURGERY, OPERATIVE	E4
UNITED STATES MC [as MeSH heading]	Z1.107.567.875
UNITED STATES [as place of publication]	Z1.107.567.875
VASCULAR DISEASES	C14.907
VERTEBRATE VIRUSES	B4.909
VERTEBRATES	B2
VIRUS DISEASES	C2
VIRUSES	B4
WOUNDS AND INJURIES	C21.866

Appendix G: Topical Subheadings with Scope Notes and Allowable Categories

abnormalities   (A1–9, A13–15)
   Used with organs for congenital defects producing changes in the morphology of the organ.

administration & dosage   (D)
   Used with drugs for dosage forms, routes of administration, frequency and duration of administration, quantity of medication, and the effects of these factors.

adverse effects   (D–E, F4, G3, H1, J)
   Used with drugs, chemicals, or biological agents in accepted dosage—or with physical agents or manufactured products in normal usage—when intended for diagnostic, therapeutic, prophylactic, or anesthetic purposes. Used also for adverse effects or complications of diagnostic, therapeutic, prophylactic, anesthetic, surgical, or other procedures.

analogs & derivatives   (D1–7, D9–26)
   Used with drugs and chemicals for substances that share the same parent molecule or have similar electronic structure but differ by the addition or substitution of other atoms or molecules. Used when the specific chemical heading is not available, and no appropriate group heading exists.

analysis   (A, B1, B3–6, C4, D, G3, J)
   Used for the identification or quantitative determination of a substance or its constituents and metabolites; includes the chemical analysis of tissues, tumors, body fluids, organisms, plants, air, water, or other environmental carrier. Applies to both methodology and results. For analysis of substances in blood, cerebrospinal fluid, and urine the specific subheading designating the fluid is used.

anatomy & histology   (A, B1–2, B5–6)
   Used with organs, regions, and tissues for normal descriptive anatomy and histology; used for normal anatomy and structure of animals and plants.

antagonists & inhibitors   (D)
   Used with chemicals, drugs, and endogenous substances to indicate substances or agents which counteract their biological effects by any mechanism.

biosynthesis   (D)
   Used for the formation of chemical substances in organisms, in living cells, or by subcellular fractions.

blood   (B2, C–D, F3)
   Used for the presence or analysis of substances in the blood; also for examination of, or changes in, the blood in disease states. Excludes serodiagnosis, for which the subheading 'diagnosis' is used, and serology, for which 'immunology' is used.

From: MEDICAL SUBJECT HEADINGS—ANNOTATED ALPHABETIC LIST, 1984.

blood supply   (A1-6, A8-10, A13-16, C4)
Used for arterial, capillary, and venous systems of an organ or region whenever the specific heading for the vessel does not exist; includes blood flow through the organ.

cerebrospinal fluid   (B2, C-D, F3)
Used for the presence or analysis of substances in the cerebrospinal fluid; also for examination of or changes in cerebrospinal fluid in disease states.

chemical synthesis   (D)
Used for the chemical preparation of molecules in vitro. For the formation of chemical substances in organisms, living cells, or subcellular fractions, 'biosynthesis' is used.

chemically induced   (C, F3)
Used for diseases, syndromes, congenital abnormalities, or symptoms caused by chemical compounds in man or animals.

classification   (A11, B-N)
Used for taxonomic or other systematic or hierarchical classification systems.

complications   (C, F3)
Used with diseases to indicate conditions that co-exist or follow, i.e., co-existing diseases, complications, or sequelae.

congenital   (C1-15, C17-23)
Used with disease headings to indicate those conditions existing at, and usually before, birth; excludes morphologic abnormalities and birth injuries, for which 'abnormalities' and 'injuries' are used.

cytology   (A-B)
Used for normal cellular morphology of unicellular and multicellular organisms.

deficiency   (D)
Used with endogenous and exogenous substances which are absent or in diminished amount relative to the normal requirement of an organism or a biologic system.

diagnosis   (C, F3)
Used with diseases for all aspects of diagnosis, including examination, differential diagnosis and prognosis; excludes mass screening for which 'prevention & control' is used. The subheading 'radiography' is used for radiographic diagnosis.

diagnostic use   (D, H)
Used with chemical compounds, drugs, and physical agents when used for studies of clinical function of an organ, or for the diagnosis of human or animal diseases.

diet therapy   (C, F3)
Used with disease headings for dietary and nutritional management of the disease. Does not include vitamin or mineral supplements, for which 'drug therapy' may be used.

drug effects   (A, B1, B3–6, F1–2, G4–12)
Used with organs, regions, tissues, or organisms and physiological and psychological processes for the effects of drugs and chemicals.

drug therapy   (C, F3)
Used with disease headings for the treatment of the disease by the administration of drugs, chemicals, and antibiotics. For diet therapy and radiotherapy, use specific subheadings. Excludes immunotherapy and treatment with biologicals for which 'therapy' is used.

economics   (C, E, F3–4, G1–3, I2, J, L, N2–4)
Used for the economic aspects of any subject, as well as for all aspects of financial management. Includes the raising or providing of funds.

education   (E–F, G1–3, H–M, N1–2)
Used for education and training programs in various fields and disciplines, and for training groups of persons.

embryology   (A1–10, A13–15, B1–2, B6, C)
Used with organs, regions, and animal headings for embryologic and fetal development; also used with diseases for embryologic factors contributing to postnatal disorders.

enzymology   (A, B1, B3–6, C, F3)
Used with organisms, except vertebrates, and with organs and tissues; also used with diseases, for enzymes during the course of the disease. Excludes diagnostic enzyme tests, for which 'diagnosis' is used.

ethnology   (Z)
Used with geographic headings to indicate the place of origin of a group of people.

etiology   (C, F3)
Used with diseases for causative agents including microorganisms; includes environmental and social factors and personal habits as contributing factors; includes pathogenesis.

familial & genetic   (C, F3)
Used for studies of genetic basis of disease; studies of diseases occurring in family groups due to environmental factors including infection, and common family dietary habits; includes hereditary disease.

genetics   (B, D6, D8–13, D24)
Used for studies of the mechanisms of heredity in organisms, or genetic aspects of endogenous chemicals.

growth & development   (A1–9, A13–15, B)
Used with microorganisms, plants, and the postnatal period of animals for growth and development; includes postnatal growth or development of organs or anatomical parts.

history   (C–F, G1–3, H–N)
Used for the historical aspects of any subject; includes brief historical notes. Excludes case histories.

immunology   (A–D, F3)
Used for immunologic studies of tissues, organs, microorganisms, fungi, viruses, and animals; includes immunologic aspects of diseases but not immunologic procedures used for diagnostic, preventive, or therapeutic purposes, for which 'diagnosis,' 'prevention & control,' or 'therapy' are used. Also used for chemicals as antigens or haptens.

injuries   (A1–9, A13–15)
Used with anatomic headings for wounds and injuries. Excludes cell damage, for which 'pathology' is used.

innervation   (A1–7, A9, A13–16)
Used with organs, regions, or tissues for their nerve supply.

instrumentation   (E1–6, F2, F4, G1–3, H, J, L)
Used with diagnostic or therapeutic procedures, analytic technics, and specialties or disciplines, for the development or modification of apparatus, instruments, or equipment.

isolation & purification   (B1, B3–5, D)
Used with bacteria, viruses, fungi and protozoa for the obtaining of pure strains; includes culture technics. Also with biological substances and chemicals for the isolation and purification of the constituents.

legislation & jurisprudence   (I1–2, L, N2–4)
Used for laws, statutes, ordinances, or government regulations, as well as for legal controversy and court decisions.

manpower   (E6, F4, G1–2, H–J, L, N2–4)
Used with disciplines and programs for the demand, supply, distribution, recruitment, and use of personnel.

metabolism   (A–D, F3)
Used with organs, cells and subcellular fractions, organisms, and diseases for metabolism; with drugs and chemicals for absorption, distribution, and excretion. For biosynthesis, enzymology, and secretion use the specific subheadings.

methods   (E1–6, F4, G1–3, H–J, L, N)
Used with technics, procedures, and programs for methods.

microbiology   (A, B1–2, B6, C, F3)
Used with organs, animals and higher plants and with diseases for microbiologic studies. For parasites, 'parasitology' is used.

mortality   (C, E, F3–4)
Used with diseases for mortality statistics, and with procedures for deaths resulting from the procedure.

nursing   (C, E, F3)
Used with diseases for nursing care and technics in their management; includes the nursing role in diagnostic, therapeutic, and preventive procedures.

occurrence (C, F3)
Used with diseases for incidence and prevalence; includes endemic and epidemic outbreaks; includes surveys and estimates of morbidity in geographic areas and in subdivisions of populations. Excludes mortality, for which 'mortality' is used.

organization & administration (I2, L, N2-4)
Used for administrative structure and management.

parasitology (A, B1-2, B6, C, F3)
Used with animals, higher plants, organs and diseases for parasitic factors; do not use if the parasitic involvement is implicit in the diagnosis.

pathogenicity (B1, B3-5)
Used with microorganisms, viruses, and parasites for studies of their ability to cause disease in man or animals.

pathology (A, C, F3)
Used for organ, tissue, or cell structure in disease states.

pharmacodynamics (D)
Used with drugs and exogenously administered chemical substances for their actions on tissues and organisms; includes effects upon metabolism, acceleration or inhibition of biological processes, and the mechanisms of action.

physiology (A-B, D, F1-2)
Used with organs, tissues, and cells of unicellular and multicellular organisms for normal function; used also with biochemical substances, endogenously produced, for their physiologic role.

physiopathology (A, C, F3)
Used with organs and diseases for disordered function in disease states.

poisoning (D, J)
Used with drugs, chemicals, and industrial materials for human or animal poisoning, acute or chronic, whether the poisoning is accidental, occupational, suicidal, by medication error, or by environmental exposure.

prevention & control (C, F1, F3, G3, I1)
Used with disease headings for increasing human or animal resistance against disease (e.g., immunization); for control of transmission agents; for prevention and control of environmental hazards; for prevention and control of social factors leading to disease; includes preventive measures in individual cases.

psychology (C, E1-6, F3, M)
Used with non-psychiatric disease, technics, and named groups for psychologic, psychiatric, psychosomatic, psychosocial, behavioral, and emotional aspects, and with psychiatric disease for psychologic aspects.

radiation effects (A-B, D, F1-2, G4-12, J)
Used for effects of ionizing and nonionizing radiation upon living organisms, organs and tissues, and their constituents, and upon physiologic processes; includes effect of irradiation on drugs and chemicals.

radiography   (A, C)

Used with organs, regions, and diseases for x-ray examinations. Does not include radionuclide imaging for which 'radionuclide imaging' is used.

radionuclide imaging   (A, C)

Used for radionuclide imaging of any anatomical structure, or for the diagnosis of disease.

radiotherapy   (C)

Used with disease headings for the therapeutic use of ionizing and nonionizing radiation; includes use of radioisotope therapy.

rehabilitation   (C, E4, F3)

Used with diseases and surgical procedures for restoration of function of the individual.

secondary   (C4)

Used to indicate the secondary location to which the neoplastic process has metastasized.

secretion   (A, C4, D)

Used for the discharge across the cell membrane, into the intracellular space or ducts, of endogenous substances resulting from the activity of intact cells of glands, tissues, or organs.

standards   (D–E, F4, G1–3, H–J, L, N)

Used with facilities, personnel, and program headings for the development, testing, and application of standards of adequacy or acceptable performance, used with chemicals and drugs for standards of identification, quality, and potency; includes health or safety standards in industries and occupations.

supply & distribution   (D–E, F4, H–J, L, N2–4)

Used for the quantitative availability and distribution of material, equipment, health services, and facilities. Excludes food supply and water supply in industries and occupations.

surgery   (A, B2, C, F3)

Used for operative procedures on organs, regions, or tissues in the treatment of diseases; includes tissue section by lasers. Excludes transplantation, for which 'transplantation' is used.

therapeutic use   (D, H)

Used with drugs, biological preparations, and physical agents for their use in the prophylaxis and treatment of disease; includes veterinary use.

therapy   (C, F3)

Used with diseases for therapies except drug therapy, diet therapy, radiotherapy, and surgery, for which subheadings exist; also to be used for articles dealing with multiple therapies.

toxicity   (D, J)

Used with drugs and chemicals for experimental human and animal studies of their ill effects; includes studies to determine the margin of safety or the reactions accompanying administration at various dose levels; used also for experimental studies of exposure to environmental agents.

transmission   (C)
Used with diseases for studies of the modes of transmission.

transplantation   (A)
Used with organs, tissues, or cells for transplantation from one site to another within the same subject, or from one subject to another of the same species or different species.

trends   (E, F4, G1–3, I, L, N)
Used for the manner in which a subject changes, qualitatively or quantitatively, with time, whether past, present, or future. Excludes discussions of the course of disease in particular patients.

ultrastructure   (A1–11, A13–16, B, C4)
Used with tissues and cells (including neoplasms) and microorganisms for microanatomic structures, generally below the size visible by light microscopy.

urine   (B2, C–D, F3)
Used for the presence or analysis of substances in the urine; also for the examination of, or changes in, the urine in diseases.

utilization   (E, G1–3, H–J, L, N)
Used with equipment, facilities, programs, services, and health personnel for discussions, usually with data, of how much they are used. Includes discussions of overuse and underuse.

veterinary   (C1–21, C23, E)
Used for naturally occurring diseases in animals, or for diagnostic, preventive, or therapeutic procedures used in veterinary medicine.

Appendix H: Alphabetic List of Topical Subheadings with Abbreviations

The following is an alphabetic list of the subheadings used in indexing with their search abbreviations and the categories or subcategories with which they may be used. ( ) gives the date of entry of the subheading into MEDLARS since 1966.

Subheading	Form for Indexing	Form for Searching	Allowable Categories
(66)abnormalities	abnorm	AB	A (except A10–12, A16)
(66)administration & dosage	admin	AD	D
(66)adverse effects	adv eff	AE	D, E, F4, G3, H, J
(75)analogs & derivatives	analogs	AA	D (except D8)
(67)analysis	anal	AN	A, B (except B2), C4, D, G3, J
(66)anatomy & histology	anat	AH	A, B1, B2, B5, B6
(68)antagonists & inhibitors	antag	AI	D
(66)biosynthesis	biosyn	BI	D
(67)blood	blood	BL	B2, C, D, F3
(66)blood supply	blood supply	BS	A (except A7, A11, A12), C4
(67)cerebrospinal fluid	csf	CF	B2, C, D, F3
(68)chemical synthesis	chem syn	CS	D
(67)chemically induced	chem ind	CI	C, F3
(66)classification	class	CL	A11, B–N
(66)complications	compl	CO	C, F3
(66)congenital	congen	CN	C (except C16)
(67)cytology	cytol	CY	A, B
(75)deficiency	defic	DF	D
(66)diagnosis	diag	DI	C, F3
(67)diagnostic use	diag use	DU	D, H
(75)diet therapy	diet ther	DH	C, F3
(66)drug effects	drug eff	DE	A, B (except B2), F1, F2, G4–11
(66)drug therapy	drug ther	DT	C, F3
(78)economics	econ	EC	C, E, F3, F4, G1–3, I2, J, L, N2–4
(67)education	educ	ED	E, F, G1–3, H-M, N1, N2
(66)embryology	embryol	EM	A (except A11, A12, A16), B1, B2, B6, C

From: MEDICAL SUBJECT HEADINGS—ANNOTATED ALPHABETIC LIST, 1984

Subheading	Form for Indexing	Form for Searching	Allowable Categories
(66)enzymology	enzymol	EN	A, B (except B2), C, F3
(75)ethnology	ethnol	EH	Z
(66)etiology	etiol	ET	C, F3
(66)familial & genetic	familial	FG	C, F3
(78)genetics	genet	GE	B, D6, D8–13, D24
(66)growth & develop-ment	growth	GD	A (except A10–12, A16), B
(66)history	hist	HI	C–F, G1–3, H–N
(66)immunology	immunol	IM	A–D, F3
(66)injuries	inj	IN	A (except A10–12, A16)
(66)innervation	innerv	IR	A (except A8, A10–12)
(66)instrumentation	instrum	IS	E (except E7), F2, F4, G1–3, H, J, L
(66)isolation & purifica-tion	isol	IP	B1, B3–5, D
(78)legislation & jurispru-dence	legis	LJ	I1, I2, L, N2–4
(68)manpower	man	MA	E6, F4, G1, G2, H–J, L, N2–4
(66)metabolism	metab	ME	A–D, F3
(75)methods	methods	MT	E (except E7), F4, G1–3, H–J, L, N
(67)microbiology	microbiol	MI	A, B1, B2, B6, C, F3
(67)mortality	mortal	MO	C, E, F3, F4
(66)nursing	nurs	NU	C, E, F3
(66)occurrence	occur	OC	C, F3
(78)organization & admin-istration	organ	OG	I2, L, N2–4
(75)parasitology	parasitol	PS	A, B1, B2, B6, C, F3
(66)pathogenicity	pathogen	PY	B1, B3–5
(66)pathology	pathol	PA	A, C, F3
(66)pharmacodynamics	pharm	PD	D
(66)physiology	physiol	PH	A, B, D, F1, F2
(66)physiopathology	physiopathol	PP	A, C, F3
(66)poisoning	pois	PO	D, J
(66)prevention & control	prev	PC	C, F1, F3, G3, I1
(78)psychology	psychol	PX	C, F3, E (except E7), M
(66)radiation effects	rad eff	RE	A, B, D, F1, F2, G4–12, J
(67)radiography	radiogr	RA	A, C
(78)radionuclide imaging	radionuclide	RI	A, C
(66)radiotherapy	radiother	RT	C
(67)rehabilitation	rehabil	RH	C, E4, F3
(80)secondary	second	SC	C4
(68)secretion	secret	SE	A, C4, D

Subheading	Form for Indexing	Form for Searching	Allowable Categories
(68)standards	stand	ST	D, E, F4, G1-3, H-J, L, N
(68)supply & distribution	supply	SD	D, E, F4, H-J, L, N2-4
(66)surgery	surg	SU	A, B2, C, F3
(66)therapeutic use	ther use	TU	D, H
(66)therapy	ther	TH	C, F3
(66)toxicity	tox	TO	D, J
(75)transmission	transm	TM	C
(66)transplantation	transpl	TR	A
(78)trends	trends	TD	E, F4, G1-3, I, L, N
(75)ultrastructure	ultrastruct	UL	A (except A12), B, C4
(67)urine	urine	UR	B2, C, D, F3
(68)utilization	util	UT	E, G1-3, H-J, L, N
(66)veterinary	vet	VE	C (except C22), E

Appendix I: Topical Subheadings by Category

A single year is the first year since 1975 the subheading was used with the category. If the subheading is not currently being used with the category, the range of years it was used since 1975 is provided.

Category A – Anatomy

75 AB /abnorm—not A10, 11, 12, 16
75 AN /anal
75 AH /anat—not A11, 12
75 BS /blood supply—not A7, 11, 12
80 CL /class—only A11
75 CY /cytol—not for subcellular terms
75 DE /drug eff
75 EM /embryol—not A11, 12, 16

75 EN /enzymol
75 GD /growth—not A10, 11, 12, 16
75 IM /immunol
75 IN /inj—not A10, 11, 12, 16
75 IR /innerv—not A8, 10, 11, 12
75 ME /metab
75 MI /microbiol
75 PS /parasitol
75 PA /pathol—not A12

75 PH /physiol
75 PP /physiopathol—not A11, 12,
75 RE /rad eff
75 RA /radiogr
78 RI /radionuclide
75 SE /secret
75 SU /surg
75 TR /transpl
75–77 UL /ultrastruct
78 UL /ultrastruct—not A12

Category B – Organisms

75 AN /anal—not B2
75 AH /anat—not B3, 4
75 BL /blood—only B2
75 CL /class
75 CF /csf—only B2
75 CY /cytol—not B2, 4
75 DE /drug eff—not B2
75 EM /embryol—not B3, 4, 5
75 EN /enzymol—not B2

78 GE /genet
75 GD /growth
75 IM /immunol
75 IP /isol—not B2, 6
75 ME /metab
75 MI /microbiol—only B1, 2, 6

75 PS /parasitol—only B1, 2, 6
75 PY /pathogen—not B2, 6
75 PH /physiol
75 RE /rad eff—not B2
77 SU /surg—only B2
75 UL /ultrastruct—not B2
75 UR /urine—only B2

Category C – Diseases

75 AN /anal—only C4
75 BL /blood
76 BS /blood supply—only C4
75 CI /chem ind
75 CL /class
75 CO /compl
75 CN /congen—not C16
75 CF /csf
75 DI /diag
75 DH /diet ther
75 DT /drug ther
78 EC /econ
75 EM /embryol

75 EN /enzymol
75 ET /etiol
75 FG /familial
75 HI /hist
75 IM /immunol
75 ME /metab
75 MI /microbiol
75 MO /mortal
75 NU /nurs
75 OC /occur
75 PS /parasitol
75 PA /pathol
75 PP /physiopathol
75 PC /prev

78 PX /psychol
75 RA /radiogr
78 RI /radionuclide
75 RT /radiother
75 RH /rehabil
80 SC /second—only C4
76 SE /secret—only C4
75 SU /surg
75 TH /ther
75 TM /transm
77 UL /ultrastruct—only C4
75 UR /urine
75 VE /vet—not C22

From: MEDICAL SUBJECT HEADINGS—ANNOTATED ALPHABETIC LIST, 1984

Category D – Chemicals and Drugs

75 AD /admin	75 CF /csf—not D25,	75 PD /pharm
75 AE /adv eff	26	75 PH /physiol—not
75 AN /anal	75 DF /defic—not	D25, 26
75 AA /analogs—not	D25, 26	75 PO /pois
D8, 25, 26	75 DU /diag use	75 RE /rad eff
75 AI /antag—not	78 GE /genet—only	75 SE /secret
D25, 26	D6, 8–13, 24	75 ST /stand
75 BI /biosyn—not	75 HI /hist	75 SD /supply
D25, 26	75 IM /immunol—not	75 TU /ther use
75 BL /blood—not	D25, 26	75 TO /tox
D25, 26	75 IP /isol	75 UR /urine—not
75 CS /chem syn	75 ME /metab	D25, 26
75 CL /class		

Category E – Analytical, Diagnostic, and Therapeutic Technics and Equipment

75 AE /adv eff	75 MA /man—only	80 RH /rehabil—only
75 CL /class	E6	E4
78 EC /econ	75-81 MT /methods	75 ST /stand
75 ED /educ	82 MT /methods—	75 SD /supply
75 HI /hist	not E7	80 TD /trends
75-81 IS /instrum	75 MO /mortal	75 UT /util
82 IS /instrum—not	75 NU /nurs	75 VE /vet
E7	78 PX /psychol—not	
	E7	

Category F – Psychiatry and Psychology
F1 and F2

75 CL /class	75 HI /hist—only	75 PC /prev—only F1
75 DE /drug eff	SPEC	75 PH /physiol
75 ED /educ—only	75 IS /instrum—only	75 RE /rad eff
SPEC	SPEC	

F3

75 BL /blood	75 ET /etiol	75 PA /pathol
75 CI /chem ind	75 FG /familial	75 PP /physiopathol
75 CL /class	75 HI /hist	75 PC /prev
75 CO /compl	75 IM /immunol	78 PX /psychol
75 CF /csf	75 ME /metab	75–77 RA /radiogr
75 DI /diag	75 MI /microbiol	75 RH /rehabil
75 DH /diet ther	75 MO /mortal	75 SU /surg
75 DT /drug ther	75 NU /nurs	75 TH /ther
78 EC /econ	75 OC /occur	75 UR /urine
75 EN /enzymol	75 PS /parasitol	

F4

75 AE /adv eff	75 HI /hist	75 MO /mortal
75 CL /class	75 IS /instrum	75 ST /stand
80 EC /econ	75 MA /man	75 SD /supply
75 ED /educ	75 MT /methods	78 TD /trends

Category G – Biological Sciences

83 AE /adv eff—only
   G3
75 AN /anal—only G3
75 CL /class
75 DE /drug eff—
   only G4-12
80 EC /econ—only
   G1-3
75 ED /educ—only
   G1-3

75 HI /hist—only
   G1-3
75 IS /instrum—only
   G1-3
75 MA /man—only G1,
   G2
75 MT /methods—only
   G1-3
75 PC /prev—only G3

75 RE /rad eff—only
   G4-12
75 ST /stand—only
   G1-3
78 TD /trends—only
   G1-3
78 UT /util—only
   G1-3

Category H – Physical Sciences

75 AE /adv eff
75 CL /class
75 DU /diag use
75 ED /educ

75 HI /hist
75 IS /instrum
75 MA /man
75 MT /methods

75 ST /stand
75 SD /supply
75 TU /ther use
75 UT /util

Category I – Anthropology, Education, Sociology and Social Phenomena

75 CL /class
80 EC /econ—only I2
75 ED /educ
75 HI /hist
78 LJ /legis—only I1, 2

75 MA /man
75 MT /methods
80 OG /organ—only
   I2
75 PC /prev—only I1

75 ST /stand
75 SD /supply
78 TD /trends
75 UT /util

Category J – Technology, Industry, Agriculture, Food

75 AE /adv eff
75 AN /anal
75 CL /class
80 EC /econ
75 ED /educ—with
   discretion

75 HI /hist
75 IS /instrum
75 MA /man
75 MT /methods
75 PO /pois

75 RE /rad eff
75 ST /stand
75 SD /supply
75 TO /tox
75 UT /util

Category K – Humanities

75 CL /class

75 ED /educ

75 HI /hist

Category L – Information Science and Communication

75 CL /class
80 EC /econ
75 ED /educ
75 HI /hist
75 IS /instrum

80 LJ /legis
75 MA /man
75 MT /methods
80 OG /organ

75 ST /stand
75 SD /supply
80 TD /trends
75 UT /util

Category M – Named Groups

75 CL /class
75 ED /educ

75 HI /hist

80 PX /psychol

Category N — Health Care

75 CL /class
78 EC /econ—only
    N2–4
75 ED /educ—only
    N1, 2
75 HI /hist
78 LJ /legis—only
    N2–4

75 MA /man—only
    N2–4
75 MT /methods
78 OG /organ—only
    N2–4
75 ST /stand

75 SD /supply—only
    N2–4
78 TD /trends
75 UT /util

Category Z — Geographic Names

75 EH /ethnol

Appendix J: Subheading Groups

anatomy & histology
  blood supply
  cytology
  embryology
    abnormalities
  innervation
  pathology
  ultrastructure

physiology
  growth & development
  metabolism
    biosynthesis
    blood/urine/cerebrospinal fluid
    deficiency
    enzymology
  physiopathology
  secretion

analysis
  blood/urine/cerebrospinal fluid
  enzymology
  isolation & purification

etiology
  chemically induced
  complications
    secondary
  congenital
  genetics
    familial & genetic
  immunology
  microbiology
    parasitology
  transmission

pharmacodynamics
  administration & dosage
  adverse effects
  poisoning
  toxicity
drug effects

diagnostic use
  administration & dosage
  adverse effects

therapeutic use
  administration & dosage
  adverse effects

therapy
  diet therapy
  drug therapy
  nursing
  prevention & control
  radiotherapy
  rehabilitation
  surgery
    transplantation

occurrence
  mortality
injuries
veterinary

organization & administration
  economics
  manpower
  standards
  supply & distribution
  trends
  utilization

(*cont.*)

FROM: NLM Initial Online Services Training Class Workbook, 1984.

Appendix K: Subheadings — Common Combinations

The groups below are commonly encountered pairings of subheadings.

(Disease A)   etiology   —where the cause-and-effect rela-
(Disease B)   complications   tionship is known

(Disease A)   complications   —where the diseases are associated
(Disease B)   complications   but cause-and-effect is not stated

(Disease)   drug therapy
(Drug)   therapeutic use

(Disease)   drug effects   (Organism)   drug effects
(Drug)   pharmacodynamics   (Drug)   pharmacodynamics

(Organ)   metabolism   (Organism)   metabolism
(Substance)   metabolism   (Substance)   metabolism

                (Disease)   metabolism
                (Organ)   metabolism
                (Substance)   metabolism

(Disease)   chemically induced
(Drug)   adverse effects

(Organ)   radiation effects
RADIATION EFFECTS
specific radiation

FROM: NLM Initial Online Services Training Class Workbook, 1984

Appendix L: Metabolism Subheading

The following words appear in titles and texts frequently. In MEDLARS they are properly covered by the subheading /metabolism.

absorption
binding
breakdown
conversion
degradation
distribution
elimination (consider /urine)
excretion (consider /urine)
incorporation
mobilization

release
secretion = /secretion
splitting
storage
synthesis = /biosynthesis
transport
turnover
uptake
utilization (but not the subheading /utilization)

The subheading /metabolism may be used with the names of organs (Category A), names of organisms (Category B), names of diseases (Category C) and names of drugs and chemicals (Category D).

PANCREAS /metabolism   (A)
SALMONELLA /metabolism   (B)
PANCREATITIS /metabolism (C)
SODIUM /metabolism   (D)

Note that concepts such as hydrolysis, oxidation, demethylation, deamination, alkylation, etc., would fall within the definition of /metabolism also if taking place in tissue. If taking place in a test tube, without tissue present, the concepts would be considered "chemical" rather than metabolic and /metabolism would not apply.

FROM: Initial Online Services Training Class Workbook, 1984

Glossary

AIM-TWX: An initial online pilot study undertaken in 1970 by NLM using the journals from *Abridged Index Medicus* (AIM) and the Teletypewriter Exchange Network (TWX) to search a small subset of MEDLINE.

ALL: A qualifying word used before a term at NLM to override the default and retrieve every searchable field in a database. It will also bypass a MULTI-MEANING MESSAGE.

Asterisked MeSH term: See Majored MeSH term or Weighting.

Backfiles: Older portions of a database that are accessed separately from the current file.

Basic index: See Dictionary file.

Bibliographic database: A database containing information about the documents in it, rather than the documents themselves.

Boolean logic: A method of logic developed by the English mathematician and logician George Boole (1815–1864). Boolean operators combine sets or terms in various relationships. The major logical operators are: "AND," "OR," and "NOT."

Cascaded tree numbers: See Pre-explosions.

Cathode ray tube (CRT): A video display device similar to a television screen.

Central concept: See Majored MeSH term.

Check tags: Routine concepts or "tags" checked for in each MEDLINE citation. These concepts include: age, sex, human, animal, etc.

COMBINE: A DIALOG command used with search statement numbers and Boolean operators.

Communications software programs: Programs allowing computers to communicate with other computers.

CRT: See Cathode ray tube.

Database: A collection of information in machine-readable form such as MEDLINE. Databases are also referred to as files.

Database access software: Programs that make it easier to use regular online systems by providing an interface between the user and these systems. This interface can translate a search statement into the command language of the system, and sometimes provide automatic dialing, access, etc. Also referred to as "front-end" or "gateway" software.

Data elements: See Fields.

Data form abbreviations: MeSH term abbreviations searchable in NLM's MED-LINE file due to the automatic online mapping from NLM's MeSH VOCABU-LARY FILE. Some data form abbreviations are searchable in DIALOG's MED-LINE.

Default: Options built into search systems that are automatically assumed when none are searched or none are specified. These options can include the database a searcher is connected to each time the user logs in, the fields that are searched when none are specified, etc.

Dictionary file: The BRS term for an alphabetical list of searchable terms in an online database. Also called basic index (DIALOG) and index file (NLM).

DOCUMENT TYPE (DT=): The prefixed qualifier (DT=) used at DIALOG's MEDLINE for six check tags: REVIEW, MONOGRAPH, ENGLISH ABSTRACT, CURRENT BIOG-OBIT, HISTORICAL ARTICLE, and HISTORICAL BIBLIOG-RAPHY.

Double-posted MeSH terms: A BRS and DIALOG software feature that allows a searcher to directly search any individual word in a multi-word MeSH term. For example, the MeSH term AORTOCORONARY BYPASS can be searched by using either BYPASS or AORTOCORONARY.

Downloading: The storing of the results of an online search in a user's own computer.

ELHILL: The name of NLM's software program for MEDLINE. An acronym for Senator Lister Hill.

End-user: The ultimate recipient of the information retrieved during an online search. The end-user may retrieve this information without an intermediary.

ENGLISH ABSTRACT: This designation indicates that an English-language abstract exists for a foreign language journal in MEDLINE. This abstract may or may not be available online.

Entry terms: *See* references to MeSH terms.

Enzyme Commission (EC) numbers: *See* Registry and enzyme numbers.

EXPAND: A DIALOG software command used to display a list of searchable terms alphabetically adjacent to a specific term from a database.

EXPLODE: A MEDLINE software command that retrieves all MeSH terms indented under a broader tree number as well as the term they are indented under. These terms are "ORed" together.

Fields: The categories of information within a single record. Abstracts, authors, and subject headings are examples of fields. Data elements are synonymous with fields.

File: *See* Database.

Free-floating subheadings: *See* Subheadings.

Front-end software: *See* Database access software.

Full-text database: A database that contains complete documents rather than only citations or references about documents.

Gateway software: See Database access software.

Index file: See Dictionary file.

Index Medicus heading (IM): A designation in *MeSH* meaning that a term can appear in *Index Medicus* as the major point of an article and has been asterisked during the indexing process.

Internal truncation: See Truncation.

INTROMED: A small MEDLINE practice file at NLM.

Iterative searching: A process that includes changing or modifying a search strategy because of something learned while online.

Logical operators: See Boolean logic.

Major descriptor: A MeSH term which never appears as a "SEE UNDER" reference. It may appear in *Index Medicus.*

Majored MeSH term: A MeSH term which may appear in *Index Medicus* because it represents a central concept in a reference and it has received an asterisk during indexing. *See also* Weighting.

Mapping: The automatic addition by computer of an appropriate MeSH term to a record.

MEDLARS: The acronym for the National Library of Medicine's *MED*ical Litera-ture *A*nalysis and *R*etrieval *S*ystem, a computerized system that produces NLM's printed and online products including MEDLINE.

MEDLEARN: NLM's computer-assisted instruction database for MEDLINE.

MEDLINE: The online database produced by the National Library of Medicine corresponding to *Index Medicus, International Nursing Index, Index to Dental Literature,* and articles from a few journals in the field of communication.

Menu-driven software: Software aided by a menu of choices for commands and formats to be selected by the user; often considered "user-friendly." *See also* User-friendly software.

MeSH headings: See Subject headings.

MeSH terms: See Subject headings.

MeSH VOCABULARY FILE: The NLM online version of *Medical Subject Headings* (*MeSH*) which automatically interacts with MEDLINE.

Minor descriptor: A MeSH term which is always a "SEE UNDER" to a major descriptor. It can never appear in *Index Medicus.*

Modem: The acronym for modulator-demodulator. A device which connects a computer terminal or microcomputer to a telephone line and converts machine-readable data to a form compatible with telecommunications equipment or vice versa.

MULTI-MEANING MESSAGE: An NLM software program message received by users when a term used in the EXPLODE strategy has more than one tree number or when a truncated term has more than one ending.

Name fragments: A field in NLM's MEDLINE and several other databases composed of the separate words in a multi-word name of substance. These words are searchable.

Name of substance: The preferred name of a chemical or drug, usually the generic name. It is directly searchable and prints out with the (CAS) registry number or enzyme (EC) number which it identifies. This information has been included in MEDLINE since June 1980.

NEIGHBOR (NBR): An NLM software command used to display a list of searchable terms alphabetically adjacent to a specific term from a database.

Nesting: The use of parentheses in a search statement having more than one kind of logical operator. Not available at NLM.

Non-Index Medicus heading (NIM): A designation in *MeSH* meaning that a term is less likely to appear in *Index Medicus* as the major point of an article and, therefore, asterisked during the indexing process.

Non MeSH terms: A designation used to group subject headings in the *Tree Structures* that can be EXPLODEd to retrieve indented MeSH terms under them, but to which nothing is indexed specifically.

Online searching: The use of computers to retrieve information from machine-readable files known as databases.

ONTAP MEDLINE: DIALOG's small MEDLINE practice file.

Positional operators: Special operators used besides the standard Boolean operators to indicate more precise relationships between certain terms of a reference. Both BRS and DIALOG have positional operators—for example, adjacency of terms is expressed with the ADJ operator in BRS and with the (W) operator in DIALOG.

Postings: The number of items listed for a term or combination of terms.

Postqualification: A procedure for taking previous search results and limiting them to specific fields or conditions without having to re-enter the initial search terms.

Pre-explosions: An NLM term for a software feature in which large tree explosions requiring excessive computer time have been exploded in advance. Called "cascaded" at DIALOG. At BRS, all tree numbers have been exploded in advance.

Priority 1, 2, 3 journals: A rating assigned by NLM to the journals it indexes for MEDLINE. Priority 1 and 2 journals get indexed in greater depth than Priority 3 journals. Priority 1 journals get rush handling due to their importance to the clinician.

Qualification: The online process of limiting a term to a specific field or fields.

QUICKSEARCH (QS): A BRS command used to attach subheadings to single MeSH terms (not EXPLODEd terms) to save computer processing time.

Records: The documents in a database.

Registry and enzyme numbers: A field in MEDLINE, searchable since June 1980, that includes Chemical Abstract Services (CAS) registry numbers and Enzyme Commission (EC) numbers. The numbers print out with the name of substance, the preferred name of a chemical or drug, usually the generic name, which they identify.

ROOT: A BRS software command used to display a list of searchable terms alphabetically adjacent to a specific term from a database.

SDILINE: The acronym for Selective Dissemination of Information, the regular, automatic updates to online searches run in any database. It also refers to NLM's SDILINE file, the name of the NLM database containing the latest month's references from MEDLINE.

Search statement: An individual, user-entered query that instructs the search program to retrieve certain records.

Search strategy: A group of search statements geared toward retrieving certain information.

SELECT STEPS (SS): A DIALOG command that is used in front of each set of terms and which gives each term within that set a separate search statement number.

Set: A group of terms or a term.

Software: A string of instructions commanding a computer to perform specific functions.

SPEC:SPEC qualif: An annotation appearing in the *Annotated MeSH*. It means that the term it describes is a specialty term only and that specialty terms can only have certain permitted subheadings.

Special list indicators: A designation given to articles from non-*Index Medicus* journals included in MEDLINE.

Stopwords: Common, non-significant words ignored by software programs in textword searching. Their number varies from vendor to vendor.

STRINGSEARCH: An NLM command used to express adjacency. First, an initial set is created, then its strings of characters can be searched field-by-field.

Subheadings: Subdivisions that group together important aspects of MeSH terms. There are currently 76. Subheadings can be searched attached to MeSH terms or searched separately—as "free-floating" or "unbound" subheadings.

Subject headings: The terms chosen from *Medical Subject Headings (MeSH)* to index the references appearing in MEDLINE and some other NLM databases. Also called MeSH terms, and MeSH headings.

Term: A subject heading (MeSH term) or any other searchable concept in a reference, such as a textword.

Textwords: The individual words found in the titles and abstracts of MEDLINE references.

Truncation: The process of allowing for alternate endings or beginnings of a term to appear without having to specify the actual variations. Though not technically truncation, allowing for embedded variable characters is referred to as internal truncation.

Unbound subheadings: *See* Subheadings.

Unqualified term: A term or a group of terms that have not been limited to certain fields.

User-friendly software: Software that is easier to use; often, menu-driven software. *See also* Menu-driven software.

Vendor: A company or organization such as BRS, DIALOG, or NLM that markets online databases.

Venn diagram: A representation of logical relationships with circles, named for the English logician John Venn (1834–1923).

Weighting: The importance of a MeSH term is indicated by whether it may appear in *Index Medicus* as a major concept of a reference, asterisked during the indexing process, or as a non-*Index Medicus* heading. *See also* Majored MeSH term.

Further Reading

Bachrach CA, Charen T. Selection of the MEDLINE contents, the development of its thesaurus, and the indexing process. Med Inf 1978 Sep;3:237–54.

Burdick AJ. Using unbound subheadings to increase recall in MEDLINE. Bull Med Libr Assoc 1983 Jul;71:282–86.

Burroughs S, Kyle S. Searching the MEDLARS file on NLM and BRS: a comparative study. Bull Med Libr Assoc 1979 Jan;67:15–24.

Charen T. Subheadings in search. Libr Network/MEDLARS Tech Bull 1971 Aug;28:5–11.

Egeland J, Foreman G. Reference services: searching and search techniques. In: Darling L, Bishop D, Colaianni LA, eds. Handbook of Medical Library Practice. 4th ed. Chicago: Medical Library Association, 1982:183–235.

Evolution of computerized bibliographies. In: Miles WD. A History of the National Library of Medicine. Bethesda, MD: National Library of Medicine, 1982:365–91.

Feinglos SJ. A comparison of MEDLINE searching—NLM vs. BRS and DIALOG. In: Snow B, ed. Database search aids—health sciences. Weston, CT: Online, 1982:37–43.

Feinglos SJ. MEDLINE at BRS, DIALOG, and NLM: is there a choice? Bull Med Libr Assoc 1983 Jan;71:6–12.

Funk M, Reid C. Indexing consistency in MEDLINE. Bull Med Libr Assoc 1983 Apr;71:176–83.

Green EW. Searching the MEDLARS file for information about the elderly. Bull Med Libr Assoc 1981;69:359–67.

Hafner AA, Haycock LA, Carroll DJ. Searching the MEDLARS special list categories. Online 1973 Jul;1:73–76, 81.

Harter S. Online searching styles: an exploratory study. Coll Res Libr 1984 Jul;45:249–58.

Hayes RH. Pricing policies for the National Library of Medicine. Ann Int Med 1984 Apr;100:601–4.

Healy PE, Knecht LS. Search hint: using date of entry (DA) ranges. NLM Tech Bull 1983 Apr;168:6–9.

Introduction. Index Medicus. (recent unbound issue).

Kelner LW. Searching the MEDLARS database: A practical guide for profilers. Rev. ed. Latham, NY: BRS, 1981.

Kenton C, Scott YB. MEDLINE searching and retrieval. Med Inf 1978 Sept;3:225–35.

Knecht LWS. Sensible searching: limiting to English language citations. NLM Tech Bull 1984 Mar;179:7-11.

Kolner SJ. Improving the MEDLARS search interview: a checklist approach. Bull Med Libr Assoc 1981 Jan; 69:26–33.

Mathews C. Supplemental training program for MEDLARS searchers. Med Ref Serv Quart 1983 Winter;2:21–30.

The MEDLINE Search Guide. New York: Online Research Systems, 1984.

MeSH introduction. Cumulated Index Medicus 1983;24:VII–XIII, or Index Medicus 1984 Jan (part 2): VII–XIII. ("black-and-white" MeSH)

Principles of indexing: parts I and II. (Videorecording) Washington: National Medical Audiovisual Center, 1976. (Contains accompanying printed syllabus)

Rizzo L. Where's that article? NLM Tech Bull 1983 Sept;173:15.

Sewell W, Harrison M. Using MeSH for effective searching: a programmed guide. Bethesda, MD: National Library of Medicine, 1975.

Siegelman DL, Kolman R, Bobka MS. Searching MEDLINE on BRS: special features. Med Ref Serv Quart 1982 Winter;1:1–22.

Snow B, ed. Database search aids—health sciences. Weston, CT: Online, 1982.

Snow B. MEDLINE on DIALOG: a guide to searching techniques. Med Ref Serv Quart 1982 Spring;1:3–37.

Tenopir C. To err is human; seven common searching mistakes. Libr J 1984 Apr 1;109:635–36.

Tilley CB, Proudman ST. General guidelines for cost-effective searching. NLM Tech Bull 1983 Aug;172:7–9.

Van Buskirk NE. The review article in MEDLINE: ambiguity of definition and implications for online searchers. Bull Med Libr Assoc 1984 Oct;72:349–52.

Werner G. Use of on-line bibliographic retrieval services in health sciences libraries in the United States and Canada. Bull Med Libr Assoc 1979 Jan;67:1–14.

Index